HODDER SCIENCE

Pupil's Book

A

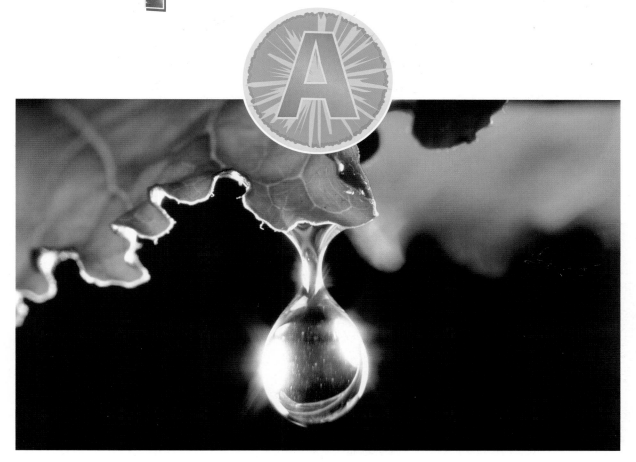

Nigel Heslop
David Brodie
James Williams

Hodder & Stoughton

A MEMBER OF THE HODDER HEADLINE GROUP

Photo acknowledgements

The publishers would like to thank the following individuals, institutions and companies for permission to reproduce photographs in this book. Every effort has been made to trace ownership of copyright. The publishers would be happy to make arrangements with any copyright holder whom it has not been possible to contact:

Action Plus (23 bottom, 69, 71 top, 74, 75, 76, 108 top left); All Action (83); Andrew Lambert (21 bottom right, 63, 70 bottom, 98, 103, 106 right, 107 all, 108 bottom right); Armagh Planetarium (148); Associated Press (139 bottom); BBC Natural History Unit (78, 126 top right); BBC Tomorrow's World (5 right); Bruce Coleman Limited (32 bottom right, 43 all, 71 bottom, 79, 121, 126 left, middle and bottom right, 127 bottom four photos); Corbis (2 right, 7 bottom, 33 top, 110, 128, 139 top); David & Helen Litt (85 top); Galaxy Picture Library (147 second down on left and top right); Hodder & Stoughton (20 top left, 33 bottom, 73, 88 right, 145 top); Holt Studios (85 bottom (both), 89 both, 127 top left); Home Office (138); Hulton Getty (23 top); Leonard Hayflick (7 top); Life File (22 bottom (both), 32 top right, 55 bottom right, 66 top, 95, 97, 108 top right, 129 middle and bottom, 134 top and bottom, 136, 142); NASA (118 right, 119 top); Natural History Museum (33 middle); Nigel Heslop (20 right, 25, 102, 134 middle, 137); Oxford Scientific Films (5 left, 88 left, 122); Photodisc (141); Press Association (58, 92); Ronald Grant Archive (130, 145 bottom); Science Museum/ Science & Society Picture Library (2 left and middle); Science Photo Library (129 top, 147 top left)/ Adam Hart-Davis (70 top)/ Alex Bartel (32 top left and bottom left, 62)/ Andrew Syred (4 middle and bottom right)/ Bernhard Edmaier (21 top right)/ CNRI (4 left)/ Corey Meitchik, Custom Medical Stock Photo (48 second from bottom)/ Dan Schechter (143)/ David Nunuk (32 middle right)/ David Parker (55 bottom left)/ Don Fawcett (47)/ Dr G Moscoso (48 third from top)/ Dr Yorgos Nikas (48 left and top right)/ James Stevenson (48 bottom right)/ JC Revy (127 top right)/ John Heseltine (120 top)/ Mark Burnett (20 bottom left)/ Martin Bond (55 top right)/ Martin Dohrn (32 middle left)/ Martyn F Chillmaid (114)/ NASA (118 bottom left, 144 bottom, 147 bottom two on left)/ Novosti (144 top)/ Peter Menzel (21 left)/ Petit Format, Nestle (48 second from top)/ Secchi-Lecaque, Roussel-UCLAF, CNRI (4 top right)/ Simon Fraser (36, 120 middle and bottom)/ Stevie Grand (106 top left)/ Tim Beddow (55 top left)/ US Geological Survey (118 top left, 119 bottom); Sue Cunningham (66 bottom); Wellcome Trust, Medical Photographic Library (22 top left, 67).

Orders: please contact Bookpoint Ltd, 78 Milton Park, Abingdon, Oxon OX14 4TD. Telephone: (44) 01235 827720, Fax: (44) 01235 400454. Lines are open from 9.00–6.00, Monday to Saturday, with a 24 hour message answering service. Email address: orders@bookpoint.co.uk

British Library Cataloguing in Publication Data
A catalogue record for this title is available from The British Library

ISBN 0 340 73722 0

First published 2000
Impression number   10 9 8 7 6 5 4 3 2 1
Year   2005 2004 2003 2002 2001 2000

Copyright © 2000 Nigel Heslop, David Brodie, James Williams

Cover photo from Holt Studios International.
Typeset by Wearset, Boldon, Tyne and Wear.
Illustrated by Bill Donohoe, Richard Duszczak, Jeff Edwards and Ian Foulis Associates.
Designed by Lynda King.
Printed in Italy for Hodder & Stoughton Educational, a division of Hodder Headline Plc, 338 Euston Road, London NW1 3BH by Printer Trento, Italy

Contents

Dedications

To my family, for their inspiration and their perspiration.

Nigel Heslop

To my wife Joan, for her patience, understanding and practical advice and, in particular, for keeping my ideas firmly rooted in the classroom, and to Laura and Sarah Grant for their expert advice in choosing the photographs for the biology units.

James Williams

To Tom, Eleanor and Claire, not so much for being supportive as for being.

David Brodie

Life

Starter Activity
What are living organisms made from?

All living things are made up of cells. This chapter will look at different types of cells and how cells make up **tissues** and **organs**.

A tissue is a set of similar cells working together to do a specific job. An organ is a group of tissues. Some organs work together to make an **organ system**.

The heart pumps **blood** around the body through a network of **arteries** and receives blood from a network of **veins**. The heart is a large muscle with four chambers. Blood carries **oxygen** around the body and brings **carbon dioxide** back to the lungs. **White blood cells** fight off infection.

The brain is the control centre of the body. It receives information and sends out instructions to the body using a network of cells called **nerves**.

The liver acts like a filter to clean our blood. It breaks down chemicals, called **toxins**, that could poison us. It also stores sugar as a chemical called **glycogen**.

The lungs take air into our body from which we take oxygen. We also get rid of carbon dioxide in the air that we breathe out.

Kidneys remove waste chemicals from our blood and produce **urine** which can be stored in our bladder.

Food is partly broken down in the stomach by **hydrochloric acid**. Chemicals called **enzymes** are added to it to help break it down.

Food is broken down in the small intestine to release chemicals our body can use including sugar, proteins, fats, vitamins and minerals, and fibre.

Most of the water in our food is absorbed back into our body from the large intestine.

Urine is stored in the bladder. It leaves the body through a thin tube called the **urethra**.

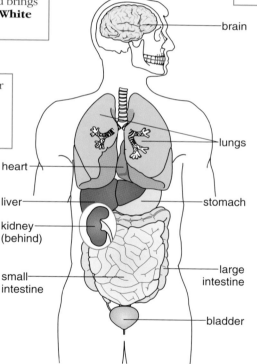

brain

lungs

heart

liver

stomach

kidney (behind)

small intestine

large intestine

bladder

Questions

1 Copy the outline of the body into your book. Close the textbook and label all the organs. Swap books and correct each other's work.
2 Which organs work together in the digestive system?
3 Which organs work together in the circulatory (blood) system?

Cells

All living organisms are made up of cells.

Robert Hooke

In 1665 a scientist called Robert Hooke published a book called *Micrographia*. His book was all about what you could see under a microscope. In this book he used the word **cell** for the first time. He was describing what cork looked like, and thought that the box shapes he could see were like the rooms that monks lived in, called cells. Today the word cell describes what all living things are made up of. Unlike Robert Hooke's empty boxes, we know that cells are not empty but full of important structures and chemicals.

Robert Hooke

Hooke's microscope

Some drawings from Hooke's book *Micrographia*

Hooke's drawing of the cells in cork

Figure 1

Cell structure

Plant and animal cells have a number of things in common and a few differences.

Figure 2 shows you what a typical animal cell and a typical plant cell look like.

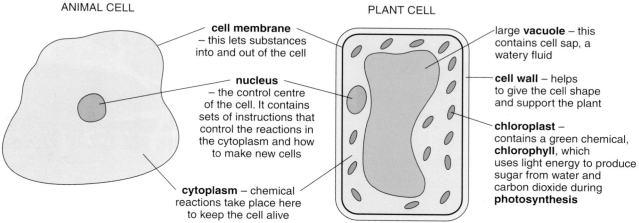

ANIMAL CELL

cell membrane – this lets substances into and out of the cell

nucleus – the control centre of the cell. It contains sets of instructions that control the reactions in the cytoplasm and how to make new cells

cytoplasm – chemical reactions take place here to keep the cell alive

PLANT CELL

large **vacuole** – this contains cell sap, a watery fluid

cell wall – helps to give the cell shape and support the plant

chloroplast – contains a green chemical, **chlorophyll**, which uses light energy to produce sugar from water and carbon dioxide during **photosynthesis**

Figure 2

Questions

1 Copy out the following table under the heading 'Cells'. Put a tick if a structure is present in the cell and a cross if it is not. Use the diagrams to help you.

Cell structure	Animal cell	Plant cell
cell membrane	✓	✓
cell wall		
cytoplasm		
nucleus		
large vacuole		
chloroplast		

2 Plants have a cell wall that helps to give the cell shape. What do humans have to give them support and shape?

3 Chloroplasts in plant cells use water and carbon dioxide to make sugar. They join these two chemicals together using the energy from sunlight. This process is known as **photosynthesis**. Where could the plant get the following:

a) carbon dioxide?

b) water?

4 As a plant loses water, the large vacuole inside its cells gets smaller, but the cells do not lose their shape because of the strong cell walls. This means that the plant does not collapse. When the cell gets more water again, the large vacuole increases in size. Draw a strip cartoon to show what happens. Write a story under each picture to explain what is happening.

Remember

Fill in the blanks in the passage below.

**cell wall   nucleus   cells   vacuole
cell membrane   nucleus   cytoplasm**

All living things are made up of _____**1**_____.

Plant and animal cells have a _____**2**_____

_____, _____**3**_____ and _____**4**_____.

Plant cells also have a _____**5**_____

_____, and a _____**6**_____. Cells are

controlled by the _____**7**_____. Chemical

reactions, which keep the cell alive, take

place in the cytoplasm.

Tissues

Groups of cells of the same kind are called a tissue. Tissues carry out different jobs or **functions**.

Different cells, different jobs!

Different cells have different jobs. Some make things, others control things. Some protect us, others provide support. They often work together in groups.

Animal tissue	Job
skin	to protect the body and stop harmful things entering
blood	to carry oxygen, carbon dioxide and chemicals from food around the body
bone	to give support
nervous tissue	to carry messages
muscle	to help us move

Plant tissue	Job
xylem	to carry water and minerals from the roots to the leaves
phloem	to carry food dissolved in water around the plant

Table 1 Some examples of animal and plant tissues

a) Sperm cells

b) Nerve cells

c) Red and white blood cells

d) Xylem vessels

Figure 1 Plant and animal cells come in different shapes and sizes

Growing tissues

Some animals and plants can replace damaged parts and tissues. Humans do this when we repair cuts and broken bones. Large parts of plants can be cut off without the plant dying. Gardeners deliberately prune some plants to make them grow.

A starfish can replace one of its 'arms' if it is eaten by a larger animal. Regrowing damaged parts is called **regeneration**. Some people think that if you cut a worm in two you will have two worms. This is not true. The top half may grow a new tail but the tail end will die.

Figure 2 The starfish will regenerate a missing arm. A person cannot do this, but we can regenerate a fingernail that gets lost in an accident.

Plant and animal tissues can be grown outside the body. Scientists do this for a number of reasons, for example to study cells better, or to replace damaged tissue. When tissues are grown like this they are called **tissue cultures**. They have to be grown in very clean or **sterile** conditions. In order for the cells to grow they need nutrients or food. A special jelly called a **culture medium** provides this. If you take the tip off the shoot of a plant and grow this in a culture medium, you can grow a whole new set of shoots, leaves and flowers. When this is planted in soil, the plant will develop roots.

Scientists can grow human skin to replace skin that has been damaged in a fire. Recently, scientists have been looking at ways of making new tissue grow over a shape. This could enable surgeons to repair tissue that has been badly damaged and help rebuild a person's ear.

Figure 3 Scientists covered a mesh in the shape of a human ear with mouse cells. As these cells grew, the mesh dissolved leaving mouse tissue in the shape of an ear. This ear was transplanted onto the mouse in the photo above. It is hoped that in the future, scientists will be able to use such technology to repair damaged tissue on humans.

Questions

1 What do we mean by a 'tissue culture'?

2 Small cuts heal leaving no marks. If you get a deep cut, what can happen when it heals?

3 Why do tissue cultures need sterile conditions?

4 Scientists might be able to grow the shape of an ear. What could be stopping them growing a finger or hand?

Remember

Unscramble the words on each line to make a sentence.

a) cells different different jobs have
b) same kind called a tissue group of cells of the are
c) called tissue cultures can be grown plant and animal tissues outside the body these are

New cells from old

Cells in our bodies are continually being replaced.

Growth

You are not the same person today as when you were born. It may sound silly, but it's true. Since you were born you have grown and developed. In fact you no longer have any of the cells in your body that you were born with! As we grow and develop, the cells, tissues and organs in our body grow and change. How do they do this? Well, cells are always being replaced and old cells die and get broken down in our bodies. In fact in the time it has taken to read this paragraph, many of the cells in your body have died and many new ones have taken their place. A normal cell does not live forever.

All of the cells in our body, except mature red blood cells, have a **nucleus**. The nucleus controls what the cell does (its function) and when and how it should divide. Look at the cartoon strip opposite to see how cells divide. Cells make copies of themselves when they divide.

In 1961, a cancer scientist called Leonard Hayflick found out that normal human cells eventually die. He also noticed that the oldest cells he grew in his lab usually died first. Hayflick suspected that cells contain some sort of clock that tells them when it is time to stop dividing. Later he discovered that cells have what he called an 'event counter' – this counts the number of times a group of cells will double *not* how long the cell has been alive. Most groups of cells can double between 50 and 100 times before they die completely. Some cells, such as red and white blood cells, can double many more times. Other cells, like nerve cells, cannot double at all. A small group of two cells that doubles three times would end up as a group of 16 cells. Two cells double to four, four cells double to eight, and eight cells double to 16.

(a)

(b)

(c)

(d)
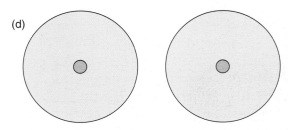

Figure 1 a) The cell prepares to divide. b) The nucleus makes a copy of itself. c) The two nuclei move to opposite ends of the cell and the cell starts to pinch in the middle. d) Two new cells are produced identical to the first cell.

Figure 2 Leonard Hayflick

Figure 3 The actor Christopher Reeve was paralysed in a horse riding accident. He damaged his nervous system in the accident and since nerve cells cannot repair themselves, he has not been able to walk since.

Questions

1 Which cells are the only cells not to have a nucleus when they are mature?

2 Red blood cells do not divide as they travel around our blood vessels. Why can't they divide here and what could happen if they did divide as they travelled in our bloodstream?

3 Cells are often given what scientists call a 'Hayflick limit', that is the number of times the cells will be able to double before they die. If a group of cells had a Hayflick limit of 5, how many new cells could one of these cells produce before the cells die? (Show how you worked this out. You might also want to make a line graph to show how many cells there are after the first, second, third doubling and so on.)

4 If you damage nerve cells they will often not repair themselves. Nerve cells cannot divide to make new nerve cells. Imagine that someone badly cuts their hand and cuts through nerve cells leading to the fingers, what might happen and what effect might this have on them?

Remember

Use the words given here to complete the sentences below.

**die   live   copies   blood   nucleus
divide   decides**

Cells do not _____1_____ forever. They make _____2_____ of themselves and die.

All cells have a nucleus except red _____3_____ cells. The _____4_____ controls the cell and _____5_____ when it should _____6_____ and when it should _____7_____.

Henrietta Lacks and her immortal cells

Cancer cells can divide forever and never die.

Henrietta Lacks was born in 1920 in a town called Clover in the United States of America. Although she died of cancer in 1953, some of the cells from her body that she donated to science are still alive and reproducing. The cells have no Hayflick limit. They have helped scientists to learn about cancer and also help doctors in their research into diseases such as polio. Henrietta's cells have made her immortal and many people's lives have been saved because of what scientists have found out through studying them.

Henrietta Lacks lived a happy normal life with her husband David, moving to the town of Turner's Station near Baltimore. She had five children and then, after the birth of her fifth child in 1951, she became ill. She was admitted to Johns Hopkins University Hospital and was found to be suffering from a type of cancer that only affects women – cancer of the cervix (the cervix is found at the entrance to the womb). This resulted in an uncontrolled growth of tissue called a **tumour**. In the 1950s, treatment for cancer was not very advanced and many women died. Today, about 4500 cases of cancer of the cervix are diagnosed in this country every year, but if found and treated in its early stages, it can be successfully cured.

Henrietta let Dr George Gey take a sample of the cancer cells from the tumour she had developed. Dr Gey was working on ways of growing human cells outside the body. Normal cells he had tried to grow did not survive long once they had been removed from the body.

The cells he had from Henrietta Lacks, however, kept on growing and dividing and did not die like samples from other people. In order to keep Henrietta's identity secret and to avoid upsetting her family, he called the cells HeLa cells. HeLa cells are still being reproduced today, nearly 50 years after her death and scientists all over the world use them in their research into cancer.

Looking for cancer

Tumours can be either **benign** or **malignant**. Benign tumours are not cancer. They can usually be removed without any problem. It is the malignant tumours which are cancer.

Cancer can often be found before the disease causes symptoms. Checking for cancer (or for conditions that may lead to cancer) in a person who does not have any symptoms of the disease is called **screening**.

Screening may involve a physical examination, medical tests or scans. During a physical exam, the doctor looks for anything unusual and feels for any lumps or growths. Examples of laboratory tests include blood and urine tests and looking through a microscope at cells. Scans involve the use of X-ray images (such as mammograms to check the breasts).

In a special kind of X-ray imaging, a CT or CAT scan uses a computer linked to an X-ray machine to make a series of detailed pictures of the inside of the body.

What is cancer?

Cancer is the uncontrolled division of cells. A cancerous cell will keep on dividing and each of the cells it produces also keeps on dividing. Eventually a tumour can form. Cancerous cells can also travel around the body in the bloodstream and new tumours can be produced at other sites in the body. Many things can cause cancer, including exposure to radioactivity, strong chemicals and too much sunbathing.

Not all cancers will lead to death. Many cancers can be treated if caught early, either by radiotherapy (killing the cancer cells with radioactivity), chemotherapy (killing the cells with powerful drugs) or removing the cancerous cells by surgery (cutting them out of the body). The likelihood of someone getting cancer will vary with age. You are very unlikely to have cancer as a child or young person. The older you are, the greater the chance of having some type of cancer. It is not just found in humans though – cats, dogs, farm animals, birds and fish can all suffer from cancer.

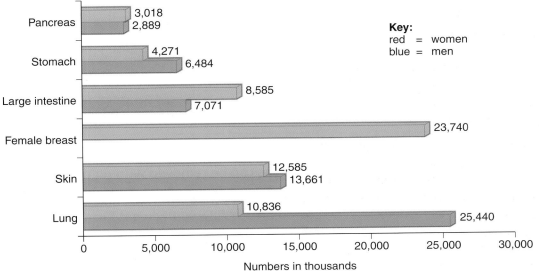

Key:
red = women
blue = men

Pancreas 3,018 / 2,889
Stomach 4,271 / 6,484
Large intestine 8,585 / 7,071
Female breast 23,740
Skin 12,585 / 13,661
Lung 10,836 / 25,440

Numbers in thousands

Figure 1 Incidences of some common cancers

Questions

1 How did Dr Gey come up with the term HeLa cells?

2 Explain what is meant by the term 'tumour'.

3 What are the three most common treatments for cancer?

4 What are the main causes of cancer that we know about?

5 There are more cases of skin cancer diagnosed today than there were 50 years ago. Why is this?

6 How do cancer cells move around the body?

Remember

Use the words given here to complete the sentences below.

successful cancer cure uncontrolled removing treatment research

____1____ is treated by killing and ____2____ the cells that are dividing in an ____3____ way. The ____4____ is very difficult and sometimes is not ____5____ . A great deal of medical ____6____ is looking for a ____7____ for cancer, but we still haven't yet found one.

Are you irreplaceable?

We can survive without many of our body parts.

Although the cells in our bodies are continually dividing, we cannot re-grow limbs or organs, unlike the starfish on page 5. If our organs become damaged, we may need an **organ transplant**.

You may be surprised to learn that you can live without quite a lot of your body. Even so, it is still best to hang on to what you have for as long as you can and look after it carefully.

Body part	How can you live without it?
skull cap	Your skull protects your brain but metal plates can be used instead.
arms	Many people have lost an arm in an accident. You can adapt to living without a limb or you can have a replacement false limb fitted.
legs	Many people have lost a leg in an accident.
liver	You can lose $\frac{3}{4}$ of your liver without serious problems. In children the liver can grow back!
spleen	The spleen breaks down old red blood cells. You can live without one.
appendix	This section of your intestine can be removed with no problems.
gall bladder	This produces bile that neutralises the acid which is added to your food in the stomach. You have to be careful what you eat but you can live without it.
pancreas	This makes enzymes that break down food. If this is removed, you have to take medication for the rest of your life.
stomach	Most of your stomach can go. It adds acid to your food but most digestion takes place in the small intestine.
large intestine	This takes water from the food passing through your body. You do not need it to live.
small intestine	Most of the digestion of your food happens here. The small intestine is several feet long and you could lose most of it, although you might have to be fed through a tube with a mixture that is partly digested. Not very tasty!
kidney	You have two kidneys and you can happily lead a normal life with just one. Damage that and you may need a replacement or some artificial help.
reproductive organs	None of these are essential to life and can be removed if they have cancer. They produce chemicals called hormones which have to be replaced.
thyroid gland	This produces chemicals that control your growth. If you have this taken away you will need medication for life.
adrenal gland	This produces hormones. Without it you will need to take hormone replacements for ever.

Table 1

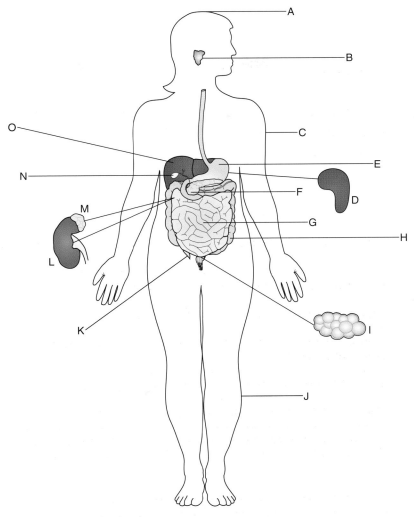

Figure 1 These are the bits of your body that you can live without.

Questions

1 Table 1 tells you which organs or parts of the body you could lose and still live a near normal life. Make a list of the parts and match them to the letters on the diagram.

2 **a)** Name three essential parts of your body that you cannot lose and stay alive.

   b) Explain why you cannot live without each of these.

3 Make a list of all the parts that can be lost and cause a person no bother at all.

4 Copy and fill in the table opposite using the information from Table 1.

Medical help needed if this body part is lost	Type of medical help needed

Remember

Unscramble these names for body parts you can do without.

NIYKED	LENEPS
HAMCOTS	XIPADPEN
GELS	RODHITY
VILER	

Finishing off!

The basic unit of life is the **cell**. Plants and animals are made up of cells. There are many different types of cell. Cells have a **nucleus** to control what they do and when and how they divide to form new cells. Groups of cells make up **tissues** and groups of tissues make up **organs**. Humans have a number of **organ systems** that allow the life processes to take place. The following systems allow life processes in humans to take place:

movement	muscle and skeletal system
respiration	lungs and cells
sensitivity	nervous system
growth	digestive system
reproduction	reproductive system
excretion	digestive, urinary and respiratory
nutrition	digestive system

As we grow and develop, our cells divide making exact copies of themselves. As the number of cells increases and their size increases, we grow larger.

If cells grow and divide uncontrollably, a cancerous growth or **tumour** may develop. There are many different types of **cancer** and many of them can be successfully treated if they are discovered in the early stages.

Many parts of our bodies can be removed and cause few problems because we can adjust to the loss. Other parts of our bodies, such as glands, can be removed, but we will need to take medicines to cope with the loss. Several parts of our bodies can be replaced by man-made substitutes, such as hip joints and lenses in our eyes.

1 Draw a typical plant cell and a typical animal cell. Label these parts on your drawings. (Some of the parts occur in both plant and animal cells.)

cytoplasm, nucleus, cell membrane, cell wall, vacuole, chloroplast

2 Explain what happens if a cell changes into a cancer cell.

3 There are three main methods for treating cancer. What are they?

4 For *each* method of cancer treatment, list the main drawbacks and advantages of it.

5 Cells divide instead of getting bigger and bigger. Draw a simple cartoon of an animal cell growing and dividing into two cells.

6 Explain why a person can live without an arm, a leg, a gall bladder or an appendix but can't live without a heart.

Web sites to visit:

Cells alive
    http://www.cellsalive.com/

The Why Files – stem cells
    http://whyfiles.news.wisc.edu/shorties/stem_cell.html

Changes

Starter Activity
On the state line

Here in Mandy's roadside café lots of materials are in use. It's the properties of materials that make each one useful in a different way. Some of the materials are mixtures, but others are pure substances.

You already know that solids, liquids and gases are the three basic states of matter.

Matter is another word for all the 'stuff' we know about.

- Melting is turning from a solid to a liquid.

- Boiling (or evaporating) is turning from a liquid to a gas.

Questions

1 Copy this table and fill it in for all the materials labelled in the picture.

Solid	Liquid	Gas

2 Explain how you know if a material is a solid, a liquid or a gas. What properties do these have?

3 How can you tell by looking if a material is melting?

4 How can you tell by looking if a material is boiling?

5 Copy this table and fill in only the correct materials in the picture.

These materials are melting	These materials are boiling or evaporating

6 Which materials are light and would float in water?

7 Which materials spread through air and smell?

8 Metal objects get slightly bigger when they are heated. What is the correct word for this?

Carnival people

All matter is made of tiny particles. They move about constantly, even in solids.

A wild time

Figure 1 Carnival at the Sambadrome

A way of thinking about particles

Solid, liquid and gas are called the three **states of matter**. They are all very different because of the way the particles move about and how they are packed together.

The particles are tiny. Smaller than anything you could imagine – far too small to see. But all particles are moving all the time.

They behave rather like the people at a crowded carnival.

Solid in the stand

The particles in a **solid** are like the people sitting in the stands at a carnival. Each person has a fixed place and the people next to them do not change. The people have little spaces between them. They are all in neat rows.

Because they are packed neatly together they are in a shape that has straight edges. The people can move about a little, backwards and forwards, to and fro, but they do not move out of their place in the crowd. The block of people always stays the same shape, even though the people are moving.

Liquid crowds

The people standing in the crowd at the carnival are like the particles in a **liquid**. They are all pushed together so that there are no spaces between them. But they are in a jumble and do not have fixed positions. The people can move past each other. With the movements in the crowd, people can change position quite a lot. They can have different people next to them. They can move past each other to get a different place. Just like particles in a liquid they will take the shape of the 'container'. It could be a long, thin pavement or a square section of space. Here it's the barriers that hold the crowd in its shape.

The performers are a gas

Gas particles are like the people dancing. They are all moving about very quickly and often bump into each other.

Gases need to be kept in a container. This is because the particles move about freely. The container is like the barriers at the sides of the procession. Gases mix easily with each other, that is how a smell spreads through air – the smell is carried by a gas. This is called **diffusion**.

Questions

1   Draw a picture of the people in the stands. The seats are so close together that their shoulders touch and their knees are against the shoulders of the people below them.

2   Imagine you are in the stands at the Sambadrome. Explain how you could move a little without leaving your seat.

3   Draw a picture of the people in the crowd as a random jumble of people.

4   Write about when you have been in crowds that are packed tightly together. Explain how you were able to move.

5   A gas would be like people running round in the school hall. Draw a picture of this.

6   What would make the people in your picture from Question 5 *have* to change direction?

7   What would be the difference to your picture from Question 5 if the people were running round on the school field?

Remember

Copy these sentences and draw pictures to show what they mean.

★   Particles in a **solid** are touching each other. They have fixed positions but **vibrate**.
★   Particles in a **liquid** are pushed together and touch, but move about **randomly**.
★   Particles in a **gas** are **separate** from each other. They move about very **quickly**.
★   Scientists call this the **Kinetic Theory**. Kinetic means movement.

A closer look at carnival people

The arrangement of particles can explain the properties of solids, liquids and gases.

Making a mind model

Figure 1 Watching the carnival from the stands

On the previous page you imagined particles of matter as people. This is the 'model' you are using to help you make a picture happen in your head.

All the particles in solids, liquids and gases have some energy. The particles are moving all the time, even in solids. This idea of particles moving is called the **Kinetic Theory of Matter**.

This 'model' can be used to explain things – like what is happening when a solid heats up.

If you make the people more excited – like when there is louder music – then they move about more. This is like making a solid more 'excited' by giving it extra energy. This makes its temperature higher and its particles vibrate faster.

Questions

Match the properties of matter for solids to sentences in Questions 1 to 4. Explain how the properties are 'modelled' by the carnival crowd seated in the stands.

Properties
  i) Solids don't mix
  ii) Solids can't be compressed
  iii) Solids have a fixed shape
  iv) Solids have a fixed volume

1 Every person has a fixed place. They are all in neat rows, in a shape that has straight edges.

2 There are no spaces between them and they could not be pushed closer together.

3 The block of people stays the same size, even though the people are moving to and fro.

4 The people next to them do not change position so they don't get mixed up.

Figure 2 Standing in the crowd at the carnival

Match the properties of matter for liquids to sentences in Questions 5 to 7. Explain how these are 'modelled' by the people standing in the carnival crowd.

Properties
- **i)** Liquids have no fixed shape
- **ii)** Liquids can't be compressed
- **iii)** Liquids can mix (diffuse) together

5 The people are all pushed together. There are no spaces between them.

6 The people are in a jumble and do not have fixed positions.

7 They can move past each other to get a different place with different people next to them.

The dancers

There are big gaps between the performers. Two parts of the carnival can mix together. The carnival procession could go through a narrower space if it needed to. This is like squashing a gas. Gases are easy to compress and they diffuse and mix.

Match the properties of matter for a gas to sentences in Questions 8 and 9. Explain how these are 'modelled' by the carnival dancers.

Properties
- **i)** Gases exert a pressure on the walls of their container
- **ii)** Gases have no fixed volume

8 They are moving about very quickly and often bumping into the barriers at the sides.

9 The barriers at the sides are needed to keep the people in place

Remember

Use the words given here to complete the sentences below.

**volume fixed shape compressed
compress diffuse pressure**

Particle ideas can explain that solids have a ____1____ shape and a fixed ____2____. Solids don't diffuse into each other.

Liquids have no fixed ____3____ but do have a fixed volume. Liquids can't be ____4____.

Gases are easy to ____5____. They exert a ____6____ on their container. They ____7____ into each other.

Figure 3 Dancers at the carnival

Hard lessons

Hardness can be explained by thinking about how strongly the particles hold on to one another in a solid. Metal particles are packed closely together and they are heavy, so metal materials have a high density.

Think about the materials you have cut up to make models in school. Some materials are easy to cut and some are hard.

Wood and plastic are easier to cut than metal. This is because the forces between particles are stronger in metals than in wood and plastic. Some wood can be pulled apart into fibres. The forces holding the wood particles together in a fibre are stronger than those holding one fibre to another.

Soft materials like wax, Plasticene and clay have particles that hold on to each other very weakly, so they can be easily squashed into a new shape. But if you bake clay models in a kiln, you get a change which makes very strong forces between the particles. Ceramic materials are very hard to cut. The strong forces make ceramic materials very inflexible but they break apart if you try to bend them.

Questions

1 A saw to cut wood is made of metal. Explain how you can tell that wood particles are held together less strongly than particles in metals?

2 There is a scale of hardness. The lowest material on the scale is a soft material called talc. The hardest material known is diamond.

Put these materials in order of hardness, starting with the hardest:

dry clay   steel drill   brick candle wax   stone   soap

3 Draw particle cartoons to illustrate the different hardness of wax and stone.

4 People say 'the hardest material known is diamond.' How would you get *evidence* to prove this statement?

Explain how you could gather evidence from a) experiments, b) other people, c) scientific sources such as textbooks and the Internet.

Figure 1   This is what would happen if you tried to saw metal with a wooden saw.

Density

A trick question often asked is 'which is heavier, a kilogram of feathers or a kilogram of stones'. The answer is they both have the same mass – one kilogram of course. But people are fooled in their thinking because stones are 'heavier for their size' than feathers.

Metals are most often heavier for their size than other materials. This is because the metal particles are packed more closely together compared to the particles in wood and plastic.

The property 'heaviness for its size' has a proper name. It's called **density**. Look at Table 1 showing the density of some objects. Density is measured in the table in 'g/cm^3'. This is how many grams each centimetre cube of the material weighs. Often density is measured as 'kg/m^3', which is how many kilograms a metre cube of the material weighs. A metre cube is almost the size of four washing machines – a big lump of material indeed!

This formula can be used to work out the density of an object.

$$\text{Density of material} = \frac{\text{Mass of object}}{\text{Volume of object}}$$

Remember

Use these words to complete the sentences

hard   volume   divided   cubic   metre   heaviness

In ____1____ materials, particles hold on to each other tightly. ____2____ for its size is called density. Density is calculated as mass ____3____ by ____4____. The units of density are kg per ____5____ ____6____ or g per cubic centimetre.

Questions

5   Use the formula above and a calculator to complete this table.

Object	Material	Mass/g	Volume/cm^3	Density/g/cm^3
wooden desk	wood	35 000	70 000	_____
key	steel	38.5	5	_____
chopping board	wood	1200	2400	_____
fishing weight	lead	22	2	_____
club hammer	steel	5800	750	_____
floor tile	marble	4000	_____	2.2
safety glasses	Perspex	_____	50	1.2

Table 1

6   When you are washing up, what are the things that feel heaviest for their size? Does this agree with the densities in the table?

7   If you threw a key and a wooden desk into a river, the desk would float. Why?

8   List the materials in the table in order of density. Use a computer to produce a bar chart (if there is one available).

Expansion

When most materials are heated they increase in size. For solids and liquids the increase is small but it carries a great deal of force. Gases expand much more.

Designer's headaches

Figure 1 Concorde in flight

Concorde, the supersonic aircraft, flies at 2400 kilometres per hour. At this speed, the outer skin of the aircraft becomes very hot; there is lots of friction with the air. In fact the outer structure of the aircraft expands by 25 cm. The inside stays the same size, as it is not hot. This caused huge problems in designing the aircraft.

Figure 2 Expansion joint of a bridge

Motorway bridges are made of big solid slabs. When they are baking hot on a summer day they also increase in length. The problem is not the increase, but the enormous force that the expansion causes. This could buckle and crack the bridge. There have to be special sliding joints built in like the ones in Figure 2. These cope with the changing forces and the changing length of the bridge.

Thermometers

Figure 3 An alcohol thermometer

When the liquid in the thermometer in Figure 3 is heated it expands up the narrow tube above the bulb. Because the tube is narrow, a small change in temperature and a small expansion of the liquid makes a big difference to the level in the tube.

glass tube
rubber bung
clamp stand
big test tube
temperature given by the level of water
coloured water
water

Figure 4 A simple water thermometer

Look at the diagram of a simple thermometer in Figure 4.

1 When the beaker of water is heated, what will happen to the level of the water in the tube?

2 This thermometer would be no use to measure the temperature in a freezer. Write two sentences to explain why.

Up, up and away

Hot air balloons are simple things. They have a gas burner, a big bag to catch the hot air and a basket. When air is hot it expands a great deal. This makes it lighter for its size (i.e. less dense) than the normal air around it. Because it is less dense, it will float up in the normal air.

Figure 5 A gathering of hot air balloons.

Ice is the odd one out

Nearly all solids expand when they melt and contract when they solidify. But the ice/water change is different.

Ice cubes always float in a glass of water. They must therefore be less heavy for their size than the water around them. Water must expand when it freezes. If you look at an ice cube tray you can see that the level has risen up in each square of the tray.

Figure 6 Because water expands as it freezes . . . icebergs float on top of the sea.

Figure 7 Because water expands as it freezes . . . the ice has swelled up inside this water pipe and made cracks in the metal.

Complete the sentences using the words below.

solids   bigger   same   expand   lot   melt

Nearly all materials ____**1**____ on heating and contract when they cool. But their mass stays the ____**2**____.

Gases expand a ____**3**____ more than ____**4**____ and liquids. Nearly all solids expand when they ____**5**____. Ice is odd. Water gets ____**6**____ when it turns into ice.

Stretchy and bendy

Solid particles are in a rigid arrangement. Liquid particles are in a crowded jumble. Gas particles whiz about apart from each other. These arrangements can be used to explain the physical properties of materials.

Figure 1 If the fillings were harder than the tooth enamel, they would damage the surrounding teeth. Dentists often use gold to replace teeth because it has the right hardness

Figure 2 Wood is flexible. This is helped because the particles in wood are long and thin so they bend without breaking.

Figure 3 Rubber is stretchy. The particles in rubber are folded up like a zigzag. When the rubber is pulled, the zigzag particles straighten out without breaking.

Questions

1 When clothes are repaired, the 'stretchiness' of the repair material has to be the same as that of the cloth. Explain why.

2 Draw pictures to show how particles are arranged in wood and rubber when they are unstretched and when they are bent or stretched.

Hitting the water

It hurts when you dive into a pool and do a 'belly flop'. But when you climb down the ladder, the liquid water is soft, not hard.

Particles in a liquid are like the pattern in a children's ball pond.

The particles are close together but in a jumble. Step into the ball pond and you can sink right through it. Your legs feel no resistance as they push the particles apart. The ball pond will take the shape of whatever room or space it is in. But if you 'belly flop' into the ball pond from high up, there is no time for the particles to push apart before they stop your fall. Ouch! That's why a belly flop into water hurts.

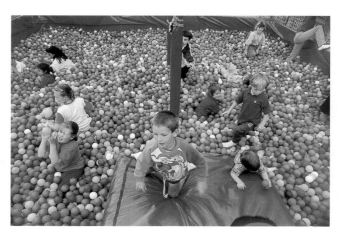

Figure 4 Children playing in a ball pond.

A soft landing

Before the invention of modern equipment, pole-vaulters had to practise their event by landing in soft sand. This has now been replaced by the modern 'crash mat'. It's full of air, and that absorbs the energy of the pole-vaulter, slowing them down to a soft landing. Sometimes the athletes even land head first!

Figure 5 A pole-vaulter from 1933 (top). A modern pole-vaulter (bottom)

Gases are the most squashable of all materials. The particles in air are separated from each other. They whiz about very quickly and collide with the walls of the container they are in, pushing it out.

If a pole-vaulter lands on the crash mat, the air particles get pushed closer together making the soft landing. The air particles move about all the time. When the pole-vaulter climbs off the mat, they push it back into its original shape from the inside. This is a result of **air pressure**. An air bag in a car does a similar job.

Questions

3   Draw a strip cartoon showing a belly flop into a ball pond. Add speech bubbles to it. Explain what has happened using scientific words.

4   What would be the effect on the pole vaulter if the crash mat was filled with water instead of air? Would this be better or worse than landing on sand? Explain why.

5   Write a short newspaper article with illustrations to explain how safety air bags in cars work. Use these ideas:

   ★   Compressed air is in a small gas bottle inside the steering wheel.

   ★   A sensor detects a crash.

   ★   The air bag inflates rapidly.

   ★   It stops the driver's head hitting anything hard.

Remember

Copy this paragraph and learn the ideas.

Solid materials stay in one shape. They can be broken up or bent by a force, but they stay the same size.

Liquids go into the shape of the container into which they are poured, but their size (volume) stays the same.

Gases can be squashed into a smaller size and shape. They will also spread out to fill all of a space.

Always moving and mixing

Liquids and gases **flow**. They take up the shape of the bottle or jar they are in.

Liquids are soft. They have no **forces** between the particles so the particles are easily pushed apart.

Figure 1 The crowd at the carnival take the shape of the space behind the barrier.

Liquids fill up whatever shape of space there is. But the particles do not stand still. They move past each other freely even though they are packed close together.

Figure 2 The dancers spread out into the space available

Gases flow, but the particles are far apart and are moving about quickly. Gases spread to take up all the space in whatever container they are in. The gas particles move about everywhere, sometimes bumping into each other or bouncing back from the walls. The force of them bumping into the walls creates the pressure.

Brownian motion

Specks of smoke or dust in a gas or liquid move about randomly. The movement of the specks is called **Brownian motion**. The gas particles are too small to reflect the light in a smoke cell, but they make the bigger smoke specks jiggle about as they hit them. You can see the movement of the smoke specks with a microscope.

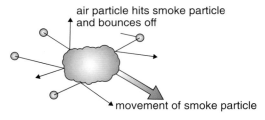

Figure 3 Brownian motion

Questions

1   **a)** Draw a picture of what a mug of sand would look like if it was poured out on to the floor.
   b) Explain the difference if the mug had contained milk.

2   Imagine the carnival at night. You would not see the dancers, only the lights if they were holding them. Describe the movement of the lights that you would see in the three areas of the carnival.

Diffusion – natural mixing for liquids and gases

Particles in liquids and gases move about randomly all the time.

If you carefully pour blackcurrant syrup into a glass of still water it forms a layer of syrup at the bottom. Leave it for the rest of the day and the random movements of the liquid particles **mix** the blackcurrant syrup and the water. At the end of the day the liquids are totally mixed. This process is called **diffusion**. Diffusion only happens in liquids and gases.

Liquids and gases mix together because the particles are moving about randomly. They can mix as they drift past each other.

Figure 4 Using blackcurrant syrup to demonstrate diffusion in a liquid.

A new smell spreads out

Liz was in the carnival procession. She was changing for the evening. She sprayed a new perfume deodorant all over herself – it was to be a night with lots of dancing. Sahera was next to her. She noticed the new perfume first and wanted to know what it was. It smelt really good. Then Jalminder, who was changing next to Sahera, noticed the smell as well and wanted to know the brand name. Finally Julia on the far side of the changing room asked where she could get some.

Inside the deodorant can, there is a gas under pressure that pushes the spray out. The can must be strong. There are many more particles hitting the inside than the outside.

Questions

3 What is the name of the process that spreads the smell?

4 How many seconds do you think it took to spread to Julia? (Use the second hand on a clock to help you guess.)

5 Draw a particles diagram to show how the perfume smell spreads through the air.

6 Draw a cartoon strip with sentences to explain how the pressure is greater inside the deodorant can than outside.

7 Make a list of all the pleasant smells that spread most easily through air.

8 'If a smell spreads really quickly, then it must be made up of small, fast-moving particles that diffuse through air easily'. Explain why this statement is true.

Remember

Use these words to complete the sentences.

Brownian motion   smell   diffusion

mix   flow   forces   collide

Liquids and gases are fluid, this means they ____**1**____. This happens because there are no ____**2**____ between the particles. The movement of the particles is called ____**3**____ _____.

Fluids will also ____**4**____ together. The process is ____**5**____. This is how a ____**6**____ spreads.

Gas pressure is caused when the particles in a gas ____**7**____ with the container they are in.

Watching changes

Have you ever seen a video running backwards? Sometimes you can't even tell that it's going the wrong way. Some scientists say that the only reason we can tell that time is passing is because everything in the world is getting more mixed together.

If you leave a bucket of **water** out in the garden for a long period of time, it doesn't stay **pure**. You don't even have to do anything to it.

At first, the water from the bucket starts to **evaporate** and makes a **mixture** with the **air**. **Acid rain** and other things fall into the water and dissolve in it to make a **solution**. If you wanted to use the water now, you would have to use **distillation** to make it pure again.

As the water continues to evaporate over time and more rain falls, the solution becomes more **concentrated**. Particles of dust from **weathered rock** and bits of earth blow into the bucket. Little organisms like algae and bacteria will be carried into the bucket on the earth and will live on the **salts** in the water. Plants like grasses or moss may take root on or near the bucket where the soil is moist.

With things to eat in the water – like the algae and bacteria – insects and snails will move into the bucket and use it as somewhere to live. They will **filter** the living things out of the water and eat them. Then larger animals – perhaps even a frog – will turn up to live off the smaller creatures.

The **metal** bucket will also be affected by the air and water. If it is made from iron, it will soon begin to **rust**. It will change colour from a silvery-grey colour to a red-brown, and the surface will become flaky, making it easier for the moss to grow.

If a video of these events was run backwards, nobody would be fooled into thinking it was running forwards.

Science uses the word **entropy** to describe this steady process of mixing up.

Questions

1 When you read the passage, does it make pictures appear in your head like a video clip? That's understanding!
Draw four 'stills' pictures from your 'video'.

2 Write down the meaning of all the words which are given in the passage above in bold text. (Count weathered rock as one thing and acid rain as one thing.)

3 Make a list of all the words given in the passage in bold which have six letters or more. Learn to spell them by the Look – Say – Cover – Write method.

4 Write a passage to describe the gradual changes you would see where you live over a period of time.

CHAPTER 2

Finishing off!

Remember

Particles hit the container walls and push on them.

PRESSURE

Gas — No shape. No size.

boiling

Particles escape into the atmosphere.

diffusion

Random motion causes mixing.

DENSITY — Solids are heavy for their size. Metals are densest.

SOLID — Fixed shapes; fixed volume.

particles — Everything is made of particles.

METALS — Conduct heat and electricity.

MELTING — Forces of attraction between particles are broken.

LIQUID

No fixed shape; fixed volume.

Questions

1 Copy the concept map and add to the illustrations and links. Try to add these ideas.

  a) Hard materials have strong links between the particles.

  b) Evaporation – one or two very excited people escape from the surface of the liquid.

  c) Freezing – particles lose energy and remain in fixed positions.

  d) Expansion of a gas to fill whatever space it is in.

2 Imagine you were making a video to show 'the particle theory' to people. Use a 'story board' method to show how you would demonstrate the changes during

  a) melting

  b) boiling.

Draw the particle performers as stick people.

3 Draw a poster for 'Carnival People' and use it to explain how this is a good model for solids, liquids and gases.

Web sites to visit:

States of matter
  http://www–wilson.ucsd.edu/education/gchem/states of matter/matter.html

Solids, liquids, gases
  http://www.dist214.k12.il.us/users/asanders/slg.html

Energy and fuels

Starter Activity
Starter Activity
People and potatoes

Plants need energy so that they can grow. People need energy to grow, to move and to keep warm.

Plants can store energy for the future. They need light to be able to do this. A potato is an energy store made by a potato plant.

A potato under the ground provides fuel for a new plant to grow. The potato is an energy resource for the new growing plant. When new shoots and roots have grown from a potato, the fuel runs out. The new plant will make its own energy stores ready for next year.

Potatoes also provide energy resources for people. Potatoes provide food. They are a kind of fuel for our bodies.

Questions

1 What do people's bodies need energy for?

2 Where can people get energy from for their bodies?

3 Where does a potato plant get energy from as it grows in a field?

4 What evidence is there that a potato runs out of energy once shoots and roots have grown?

Temperature changes

Temperature is a variable that we can measure using thermometers.

Figure 1

'Hungry?' said Chris.

'You bet,' I said.

'OK, it won't be too long. We've just got to let the oven warm up, then the pizza will start to cook.'

'How long will that be?' I asked.

'It'll be a few minutes before the oven gets to 180°C. Then it will be hot enough and we can put the pizza in. It'll just need 20 minutes more after that.'

Temperature is something that changes. It is also something that we can measure. It is a **variable**.

Every measurement of temperature is not just a number but has a **unit** as well. When we say the temperature of the oven is 180°C, the number is 180 and the unit is °C, which stands for **degrees Celsius**.

We can change the temperature of something by heating it. The hot oven heats the pizza. The pizza might have a temperature of only 4°C when we put it into the oven, but it rises to 180°C.

When we take the pizza out of the oven its temperature starts to fall. If we leave it for too long it might fall to the same temperature as the room around it – usually about 20°C. Though the temperature of the pizza would be as warm as the air in the room, it's not so good to eat and we say it's 'gone cold'.

Measuring temperature

We can use **thermometers** to measure temperature. A thermometer is a **measuring instrument**. The most common kind of thermometer is a glass tube with a **bulb** at one end. Inside the bulb is a liquid. This is usually **alcohol** or **mercury**. When the temperature of the liquid changes, it **expands** and spreads along the inside of the tube. The tube has markings along the outside, and the main markings are numbered. The markings and numbers are called a **scale**. We can look at the numbers to find out the temperature in °C.

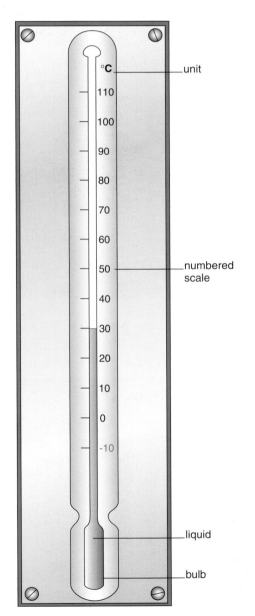

Figure 2 A liquid thermometer

1 What unit do we use for measuring temperature?

2 What measuring instrument do we use for measuring temperature?

3 What liquids might you find inside a thermometer?

4 What happens to the liquid in the thermometer when the temperature gets bigger?

5 How much did the temperature of the pizza change while it was in the oven?

6 How much does the temperature of a pizza change when it cools from 180°C to 20°C?

7 Draw a thermometer scale in your book. Go from 0°C to 100°C. Use 1 cm to equal 10°C. Mark the freezing point of water on your scale.

8 Mark the boiling point of water on your scale.

9 Mark today's temperature on your scale.

Remember

Use these words to complete the sentences.

**degree Celsius   bulb   scale   mercury
measuring   variable   thermometer
expands   alcohol   unit**

Temperature is a changing quantity called a
_____1_____. We use a _____2_____ instrument
called a _____3_____ to measure it. The
_____4_____ for measuring temperature is
called a _____5_____. A
thermometer has a _____6_____ that contains a
liquid such as _____7_____ or _____8_____. The
liquid _____9_____ when the temperature gets
higher. The liquid moves along a _____10_____
on the thermometer.

Energy from the Sun

Solar cells and the leaves of plants take energy from the light of the Sun. The Sun is also the source of other energy resources.

Figure 1 For some villages and homes, **solar cells** are the main **energy resource**. Solar cells provide electricity, like batteries do. But they only work when light is shining on them. The light provides the energy to make them work. We need energy for heating and working machinery in our homes.

Figure 2 Plants and solar cells both have large flat surfaces. The plant's surfaces are its leaves. Leaves absorb light and gain energy. **Photosynthesis** is the name we give to the way plants use energy from light to build up their energy resources. Plants need energy to grow and to get water from their roots.

Figure 3 Plants provide the energy resources that animals need to live and grow. Cows eat grass nearly all day long so that they have enough energy to live. Cows need energy to keep their bodies warm and to grow and move.

Figure 4 Food – an energy resource provided by the light of the Sun.

Figure 5 Trees use energy from the light of the Sun to grow. We can use the trees as fuel. Fuel made from material that has been alive, like trees, is called a **biomass energy resource**.

Figure 6 In some places in forests and swamps, layers of dead trees and other plants build up. Eventually, the layers might be buried by mud or sand.

Figure 7 This coalminer is deep underground, digging out coal formed from layers of plants that died millions of years ago.

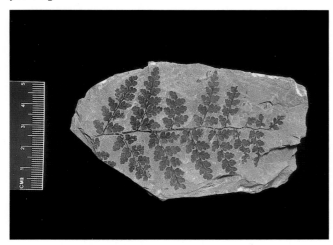

Figure 8 Sometimes you can still find signs of the old plants in the coal. This is a **fossil** of a leaf that grew a very long time ago – before there were even any dinosaurs. Coal is a **fossil fuel**.

Figure 9 The energy of the Sun creates winds. We can use **wind generators** to provide electricity.

Questions

1 **a)** Where does a cow get its energy from?
   b) Where do you get your energy from?

2 **a)** Name two similarities between solar cells and leaves.
   b) Name three differences.

3 We could burn dried sewage as a fuel.
   a) What kind of energy resource is sewage?
   b) Do you think that this would be a good idea?

4 Why is coal called fossil fuel?

5 **a)** Make a list of as many different energy resources as you can. Here are two to get you started: food, coal.
   b) Can you think of any energy resources that are not created by the energy of sunlight?

Remember

Complete the sentences by unscrambling the letters.

There are many kinds of energy resource. Plants carry out <u>SHINY TEETH SOOP</u> to build up their energy resources from the light of the Sun. Our <u>DOFO</u> is the energy resource that our bodies need.

We can burn plants. They provide a <u>I SOB SAM</u> energy resource. Plants that have been buried in layers underground can turn into coal. Coal is a <u>LOSS IF</u> fuel.

Batteries and <u>ALSO R</u> cells provide energy for electric circuits. The energy of the Sun also creates winds. We can use wind <u>RONG EATERS</u> to take advantage of this energy resource.

Electric choices

We can use different energy resources to generate electricity. Some of the resources are renewable, some are not.

Renewable and non-renewable

Have you flicked a switch today? What happened? You'll probably flick some more before the day is over. Lights will go on and off, music and voices will start and stop. You'll enjoy the power.

But it's not all good news. Electricity is generated in power stations. Most power stations burn a lot of fuel – usually coal, oil or gas. The fuel comes from under the ground.

One day the fuel under the ground will all be used up and there is no way to replace it. It is **non-renewable**. Also, burning fuels produces pollution. Gases go into the atmosphere where they can do harm.

Some energy resources are **renewable**. They will not run out. As long as the Sun shines there will be winds in the Earth's atmosphere. Energy resources like wind don't pollute the atmosphere.

So it's our choice. We could carry on just as we are now – flicking switches whenever we want for light, warmth and entertainment. Or we could stop using electricity. Or we could use more electricity that is generated without burning fuels. Some of the choices are shown below.

Energy resource	Renewable or non-renewable	Pollution level	Advantages
Coal is a **fossil fuel** made from plants that were buried many millions of years ago. Burning coal produces steam that turns **generators** in power stations.	Non-renewable	Very high	There is a lot of coal still in the ground. It is quite cheap to use in very large power stations.
Gas is a fossil fuel. Burning gas produces steam that turns generators in power stations.	Non-renewable	High	Cheap to use in large and medium-sized power stations.

Energy resource	Renewable or non-renewable	Pollution level	Advantages
Oil is another fossil fuel. Burning oil produces steam that turns generators in power stations.	Non-renewable	Very high	Moderately cheap to use in large and medium-sized power stations.
Biomass – plant and animal waste material, including dead plants and sewage. Burning biomass produces direct heating or steam to turn generators in power stations.	Renewable	High (but by always growing new plants a lot of pollution is taken out of the air)	If we grow plants to replace ones that are used then biomass energy need never run out.
Wind – energy of moving air used to turn wind generators.	Renewable	Low – but wind generators can spoil the peace of the countryside.	Wind will blow for billions of years. There is no burning involved.
Solar cells – energy straight from the Sun.	Renewable	Very low – they don't produce any direct pollution	Energy from the Sun will last for billions of years. There is no burning involved.

Table 1

Electric choices continued

We all want the benefits that come with having a big energy supply. We want the light, heat, transport and entertainment. But, as you can see from Table 1 on pages 34 and 35, there are problems as well. Fossil fuels are our main energy resource, but they have their problems.

The first problem with fossil fuels is that they produce pollution when we burn them. In cities they can create **smog**. This is a smoky fog – it is very bad for you if you breathe this in. Fossil fuels can also damage the countryside by making **acid rain**. Acid rain damages trees and kills fish in lakes. It can also damage bricks and stones of buildings. Burning fossil fuels also produces a lot of **carbon dioxide**. That goes into the Earth's atmosphere – the air that surrounds the planet. The change in the atmosphere makes the Earth warmer, causing **global climate change**. This will go on for as long as we burn the fossil fuels. We don't know what the final results will be.

The second problem with fossil fuels is that they are non-renewable. We've already used up a lot of the world's oil and gas. Future generations of people will have no fossil fuels to use.

Fossil fuels are non-renewable because they were formed millions of years ago. The supply of coal, oil and gas will not last much longer unless we do not use them so much.

Fossil fuels are the remains of plants and animals that lived in the sunshine millions of years ago. These remains have been buried in rock and preserved. We use oil rigs and coal mines to get them out of the ground.

Figure 2 Pollution from burning fuel can come back to ground level as acid rain. It can damage trees and kill fish.

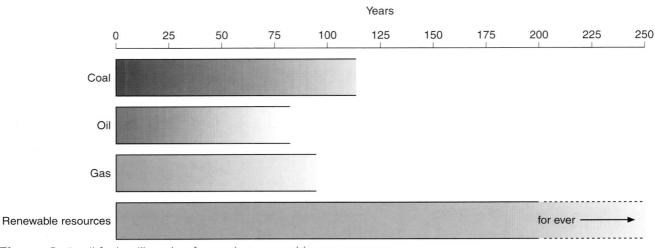

Figure 1 Fossil fuels will not last forever but renewable resources can.

Every choice has its problems. None of the ways of generating electricity is perfect. Different generating methods should be compared for:

- how much they cost to build and run
- how reliable the supply would be
- how much they damage the environment.

Energy source for generating electricity	Advantage	Disadvantage
Coal	Cheap to run, cheap to build	Acid rain and global warming
Oil	Cheap to run, quick to start up	Acid rain and global warming
Gas	Very cheap to run, very quick to start up	Global warming
Nuclear	Cheap to build and run	Long-term danger of waste leaking into the environment. Catastrophic accidents
Hydro-electric	No fuel costs. Quick to start up. Leisure use of lakes	Very expensive to build. Destroys countryside
Wind	No fuel costs. Can be built any size	Takes up a lot of space: noisy and ugly. Unreliable supply
Wave	No fuel costs	Very expensive to build and unreliable supply
Tidal	Regular supply four times a day. Low running costs	Very expensive to build. Destroys habitats, not many suitable locations
Solar – electric	Can be installed anywhere. Small generators possible. No running costs	Very expensive. Only works during the day
Solar – heating	No fuel costs	Unreliable. Energy very dilute, difficult to generate electricity

Questions

1 How would you cope without electricity? Write down three things that you would have to give up.

2 Look back at Spread 3.3. How many different energy resources are mentioned? Sort them into two lists: renewable and non-renewable.

3 Why do we use more coal than wood in power stations?

4 What are the disadvantages of using
   a) coal?
   b) wind generators?

5 Which of the energy resources in Table 1 on pages 34 and 35 are fossil fuels? Where do they come from? What are the harmful effects of burning them?

6 Are we being selfish in using up fossil fuels now and not leaving them for future generations of people?

7 Are we being selfish in burning fossil fuels and changing the atmosphere, when we don't know what effects this will have on the future of the world's climate?

Remember

Use these words to complete the sentences.

**resources   non-renewable   renewable
generate   fossil**

Oil, coal, gas, biomass, wind, moving water and solar cells are all energy ____1____. We can use them all to ____2____ electricity. Oil, coal and gas are ____3____ fuels. They are made from dead plants and animals that became buried in the ground many millions of years ago. We are digging up these fuels very quickly and they cannot be replaced. They are ____4____. Biomass, wind, water and solar cells are all ____5____ energy resources. They will not run out.

Sunshine

Have you ever wondered where all our energy comes from? If you think the answer is the Sun, you would be nearly correct. Except for nuclear energy and geothermal energy, all our energy *does* come from the Sun. Geothermal energy comes from radioactive materials heating rocks in the Earth's crust.

In August 1999 there was a total eclipse of the Sun that was visible in Devon and Cornwall. The temperature dropped and animals started to get ready for the night even though it was only 11 a.m. The most unusual thing was how nervous people felt as the Sun disappeared, and how happy they felt when the Sun reappeared.

The Sun is our nearest star. It is at the centre of our Solar System. Early civilisations, like the Incas who lived in Peru in South America around 500 years ago, worshipped the Sun – it was their god. All of us worship the Sun to some extent. On a sunny day we feel happier and play in the sunshine. Can you imagine the Sun being switched off? What would happen to life on Earth?

At the centre of the Sun is its **core**. This core takes up about one tenth of the Sun's radius. Scientists think the temperature in the core is about 15 million °C. The visible surface of the Sun is called the **photosphere**. This is the part that sends us all our heat and light. The temperature at the surface is only 6000°C!

Sunspots are darker areas which appear on the surface in cycles of about 11 years. Sunspots are a little cooler than the surrounding photosphere. They give rise to bright eruptions called **flares** on the Sun's surface. These flares send charged particles towards the Earth which can cause interference with radio communications.

During solar eclipses, a bright red region called the **chromosphere** can be seen. Normally the Sun's light is too bright for us to see it. The chromosphere is a region of not very dense gas less than 100 km thick. The chromosphere gives rise to **prominences**. These are glowing gas jets ejected from the Sun to heights of over 300 000 km. Beyond the chromosphere is the **corona**. The corona, like the chromosphere, is only visible during a solar eclipse.

The Sun's fuel is hydrogen gas. We think of the Sun as a ball of fire, but that is totally wrong. If it was a ball of fire it would have lasted less than 50 years, but it's been there for 10 billion years. Sunshine is produced by **nuclear fusion**. This is when hydrogen nuclei are rammed together to form a larger helium nucleus. During fusion, a little of the mass of the hydrogen fuel is converted to energy. Every second, the Sun loses over 4 million tonnes of mass which is transferred as energy. This energy is the Earth's major energy source and is what keeps you alive. What happens to this energy when it arrives at Earth?

Questions

1 Make a list of the words in bold and write their meanings next to them.

2 Write a *new* sentence using each word in the list.

3 Draw a cross-section through the Sun.

Fuels

We can measure the energy values of different fuels.

Fuels provide energy when they burn. They heat their surroundings. We can use the heating effect to make fuels do work for us. In a car engine, air and a little bit of fuel get very, very hot. They get so hot that there is a small explosion. The explosion pushes a piston and that's what makes the wheels go round. Only small amounts of fuel burn at a time. Each small explosion doesn't last very long. But there are a lot of explosions, one after the other.

spark plug

the explosions make the engine HOT

cylinder

explosion of fuel and air

the explosions do work to move the piston

piston

crankshaft – connected through the clutch and gears to the car's wheels

explosions inside a car's engine make its wheels go round

Figure 1 Inside a car engine

Most cars use petrol as their fuel. Petrol comes from oil. That means that petrol is a fossil fuel. Some cars run on diesel which is also a fossil fuel. Cars can also use alcohol as a fuel. Some can even use **methane**, which is the name of

the gas that we use as a fuel for gas cookers and gas fires.

Different fuels have different **energy values**. You can measure the energy value of a fuel by measuring how much it heats. It's possible to burn fuel and see how much it heats some water. To compare fuels in this way it's important to make **fair tests**. That means using the same amount of fuel for each test. It also means using the same amount of water.

We can measure the amount, or mass, of fuel in **grams** or **kilograms**. A kilogram is a thousand grams.

Water is a liquid, and we can measure the amount, or volume, of water in **millilitres**.

WATER

HEATING

FUEL

Figure 2

The energy values of some fuels are shown in Table 1.

Fuel	Energy value in megajoules per kilogram
hydrogen	140
methane	52
petrol	48
coal	35
butter	34
sugar	17
wood	13

Table 1

Notice that the energy value of fuel has a complicated unit. The unit of energy is called a **joule**, or J for short. Mega means a million of something, so a **megajoule** is a million joules. The energy value of coal is 35 megajoules per kilogram. That means that a kilogram of coal provides 35 megajoules of energy.

Figure 3 Coal, one of our main energy resources. This pile of coal, around 35 kg, would provide 1225 megajoules of energy.

Remember

Use the words below to complete the sentences.

**megajoule   joule   fair test   methane
gram   millilitre   energy values
kilogram**

We can measure energy using a unit called a
____**1**____. One million joules can also be
called one ____**2**____.

We can measure an amount (mass) of coal
using a unit called a ____**3**____ or a unit
called a ____**4**____.

We can measure an amount (volume) of water
using a unit called a ____**5**____.

____**6**____ is a fuel that many people use at
home. We can compare the ____**7**____
_____ of different fuels by seeing how
much they heat water. We have to make sure
that we carry out a _____**8**_____.

Questions

1 Which of the fuels in Table 1 can you use for your body?

2 Make a bar chart to show the energy values of different fuels. If you can, use a computer to help you with this.

3 What do you normally call 'methane' in everyday language?

4 Match up the units to the quantities that they measure:

energy   millilitre
amount (volume) of water   megajoule per kilogram
amount (mass) of coal   joule or megajoule
energy value of fuel   gram or kilogram

5 Which fuel has the highest energy value?

6 Copy and complete:

The energy value of hydrogen is _____ times as big as the energy value of coal.

7 How many joules are there in a megajoule?

8 How many grams would you expect there to be in a megagram?

Finishing off!

★ We can use a wide variety of **energy resources**, including oil, coal, gas, biomass, food, wind, waves and batteries. In power stations, fuels are burned to make steam. The steam blasts at turbines that make generators go round.

★ Almost all of our energy resources are provided by the Sun. Oil, coal and gas provide us with energy from the Sun that was stored by plants that grew millions of years ago.

★ Energy resources like wind, solar energy and biomass are **renewable**. The Sun keeps on renewing these energy resources.

★ Fossil fuels are **non-renewable** energy resources. Once we have used them we cannot use them again.

★ You have the benefit of electricity that's generated in power stations.

Questions

1 **a)** Name a fuel that power stations can use.
   b) Where does the fuel come from?
   c) What happens to the fuel when the power station uses it?
   d) What problems are caused?

2 **a)** Make a list of the ways in which you have used electricity so far today.
   b) Which of the ways you've listed use batteries as their energy sources?
   c) Which use generators in power stations?
   d) Would you like to live without the benefits of electricity?

3 Imagine that you are writing to your local paper about your worries concerning the world's energy resources. In your letter you need to explain what you are worried about. You need to say what you think should be done by
   a) you
   b) other local people
   c) national politicians
   d) people all around the world.

4 Design a system to provide heating and electricity for a small village in an isolated valley high up in the mountains. The village has

   ● a small river running through a steep-sided valley

   ● 200 days of sunlight per year

   ● strong steady winds on the mountain tops

   ● lots of forests growing on the sides of the valley.

Explain how each of these energy sources can be used. List the advantages and disadvantages of each energy source.

Web sites to visit:

Science Across The World – Renewable Energy
   http://www.scienceacross.org/english/the–topics/index.html

The International Solar Energy Homepage
   http://www.ises.org/

CHAPTER 4 Reproduction

Starter Activity
Growing up

This chapter will look at reproduction in animals and humans and how we change, both physically and emotionally, as we grow from a baby to an adult.

All animals, and plants for that matter, produce offspring that will grow into adults.

Questions

1 The pictures above show a variety of animals and their offspring. Can you match the offspring with the adult? You may have done something similar in your last school, but remember that not all offspring look like small versions of the adults. Some can be quite different. If you can, try and put the correct name for the offspring, for example, cats produce kittens.

2 Put these in the correct order: adult, child, baby, adolescent.

3 Draw a time line to show how the stages in Question 2 relate to age.

4 Put these stages for plants in the correct order:

seed dispersal   germination
seed production   pollination
fertilisation

5 What conditions are best for a seed to germinate?

Starting a new life

Male and female reproductive organs are very different.

Becoming a parent is a big responsibility. Looking after babies – feeding them, changing nappies and making sure that they are warm and safe – is a full-time job. A new life begins when a sperm cell from the father joins with an egg cell from the mother. This process is called **fertilisation**. In mammals it happens inside the female's body.

Lots of people get embarrassed when they are learning about or discussing their reproductive system. This is normal and it's the way that everyone feels. Our culture keeps its reproductive systems private as special places away from touch and sight. We have developed this approach over thousands of years, and we respect this way of doing things. As a result, we only know about our own type of reproductive system, male or female. We learn about the other type from books.

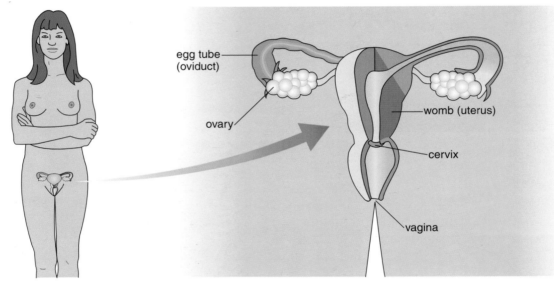

Figure 1 The female reproductive system

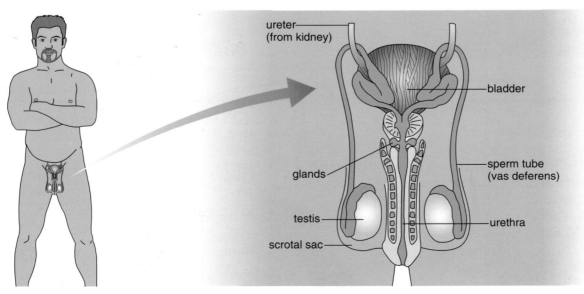

Figure 2 The male reproductive system

Producing sperm and egg cells

Egg cells are made inside the **ovaries**. When a girl reaches puberty, her ovaries start to produce egg cells. In adults, one egg is released each month. In young girls the release of eggs can be irregular but it usually settles down once the girl has fully matured. The egg cell passes down the egg tube or **oviduct**. If it meets with a **sperm cell** and joins with it, fertilisation takes place and the egg can begin to divide. The fertilised egg will enter the **womb** where it attaches itself to the wall of the womb. It may then continue to divide and grow into a baby, being born about nine months later.

Sperm cells are made in the man's **testis** (the plural is testes). Sperm cells are very sensitive to temperature. A man's body temperature is too high for sperm cells to live and reproduce so the testis hangs outside the body in a sac of skin – the scrotal sac or **scrotum**. When sperm cells are produced, they pass through the sperm tube or **vas deferens**. As they pass the glands underneath the **prostate gland**, fluids are added which keep the sperm cells alive. The sperm and the fluid together are known as **semen**.

Remember

Draw, label and learn the diagrams of the male and female reproductive systems.

Questions

1 Complete Table 1 below.

Name	Male or female?	What it does
oviduct	female	
	male	carries the sperm from the testes
	male and female	stores urine
gland		adds fluid to sperm to make semen
scrotal sac	male	
womb (uterus)		

Table 1

2 Where are the sperm produced in the male?

3 Where are the eggs produced in the female?

4 Why are the testes outside the male body in a sac of skin?

5 What is the name for the sperm and the fluid that keeps it alive?

6 In what part of the female is sperm deposited?

7 How does the sperm get into the womb?

8 How do the eggs get to the womb?

9 Make a list of all the words in bold in the text and learn their meanings.

10 Draw an egg cell at the moment of fertilisation.

11 Imagine having to look after a fragile thing, such as an uncooked egg, all day long. This is like caring for a baby. Write about how you would keep and protect it:

- on the journey to school
- during lessons
- at lunchtime and in the dinner queue
- when you are out at play.

Fertilisation

Fertilisation is the joining together of a sperm cell and an egg cell.

For fertilisation to happen, the sperm and egg must come into contact with each other. When people have sexual intercourse or 'make love' it allows the egg cell and the sperm cells to come into contact with one another. Sexual intercourse is not just about having babies. Men and women will have sexual intercourse for pleasure and for showing their love and commitment to their chosen partner.

During sexual intercourse, the man will become excited and his penis becomes stiff or erect. This happens because it fills with blood. When a woman becomes excited she produces a fluid that lubricates the vagina and the entrance to the vagina. The man's penis can be inserted into the vagina and moved in and out. This increases the pleasure for the man and woman and eventually the sperm are pumped into the vagina in the semen as the man ejaculates.

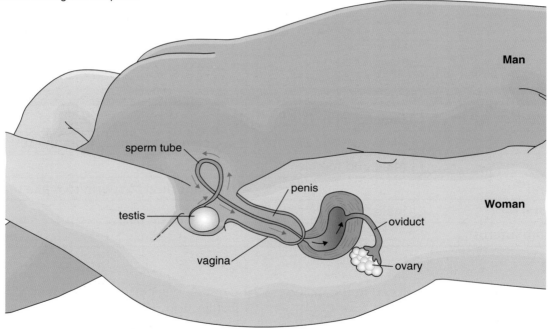

During sexual intercourse the man's penis becomes stiff. This is due to blood flowing into the penis.

When the woman becomes excited she produces a fluid in the vagina.

Man

Woman

sperm tube

penis

testis

oviduct

vagina

ovary

The penis can now slip into the vagina. It is moved backwards and forwards to give the man and woman feelings of pleasure.

Eventually the sperms are pumped from the testis through the penis into the vagina.

Figure 1 The position of the male and the female during sexual intercourse

The sperm then swim from the vagina into the womb and eventually reach the oviduct. If there is an egg in the oviduct or womb it could be fertilised by a sperm and the woman will become pregnant. The fertilised egg will carry on down the oviduct and attach itself to the wall of the womb where it will eventually grow into a baby.

Figure 2 The egg is many times larger than the sperm.

Questions

In a small group talk sensibly about the following things. You may feel more comfortable writing down your thoughts or discussing them with a close friend rather than speaking them aloud.

1   Do girls and boys act or think differently from each other? How? Why?

2   At what age do you think a person is ready to be a parent?

3   At what age do you think a person is ready to have sex?

4   What do you think are the qualities that a parent should have?

Remember

Use these words to complete the sentences below.

**inside   fertilisation   intercourse
womb   swim   pregnant**

Sexual ____1____ can make the female partner become ____2____. Sperm cells have to be able to ____3____ quite a long way ____4____ the female body for this to happen.

Successful ____5____ takes place in the oviduct or ____6____.

Growing in the womb

A single fertilised cell grows into a foetus inside the womb.

Once a fertilised egg settles in the wall of the womb, it begins to grow and develop into a baby. At first it is just a ball of cells and the cells divide just like the ones we discussed on page 6. After about 4 weeks it is possible to see the head area developing and some tiny stumps that will develop into the legs and arms.

Look at the series of photos and make a table in your book. In one column list the number of days after fertilisation and in the next column describe what the developing baby looks like. To begin with, the ball of cells is called an **embryo**. Once you can make out a head, arms, legs etc. and recognise what type of animal it is, we call it a **foetus**.

	Number of days after fertilisation	Description of embryo/foetus
	4	
	6	

Figure 1

Figure 2 The developing foetus at: a) 4 days, b) 6 days, c) 28 days, d) 8 weeks, e) 15 weeks and f) 23 weeks

As the baby grows in its mother's womb, it needs to be fed, have a supply of oxygen, be protected from harmful infections and get rid of waste products. In order to do this a round disc-like organ – the **placenta** – grows on the surface of the womb. This is connected to the growing baby by a cord – the **umbilical cord**. The placenta is rich in blood vessels. The vessels have thin walls that allow oxygen and chemicals that the baby needs for energy and growth to pass from the mother's bloodstream into the baby's bloodstream. Any waste that the baby produces while it grows passes down the umbilical cord and across to the mother's bloodstream for the mother to get rid of. The placenta can stop some harmful substances and some bacteria from passing into the baby, but it cannot prevent everything. For example, alcohol can pass from the mother into the baby and this can harm the baby as it grows. Harmful chemicals in cigarette smoke also pass into the baby's bloodstream and can cause problems.

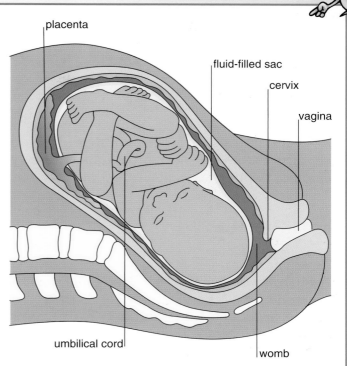

Figure 3 A baby in its mother's womb

Questions

1 What is the difference between an embryo and a foetus?

2 After how many weeks do you think the embryo should be called a foetus?

3 How does the growing foetus get a supply of oxygen and nutrients?

4 Why does the growing foetus need the mother to eat sensibly and healthily during pregnancy?

5 The foetus sits inside a water-filled sac until it is ready to be born. How could this offer the foetus protection?

6 Why are pregnant women advised not to smoke or drink during pregnancy?

7 How is the embryo connected to the placenta?

8 What happens to this connection during birth?

9 Why is the connection no longer needed?

Remember

Use these words to complete the sentences below.

blood	umbilical	fertilised
mother's	baby's	placenta
oxygen	embryo	baby

The ____1____ egg cell grows and divides to form an ____2____. It grows inside the ____3____ womb.

The mother's ____4____ stream and ____5____ bloodstream are separate, but food and ____6____ can be transferred to the ____7____ via the ____8____. The connection is called the ____9____ cord.

10 What materials are transferred from the baby's blood to the mother's blood in the placenta?

11 Draw a picture of what twins would look like in a womb. Remember there will be two placentas.

Growing up is hard to do

Boys and girls go through a number of changes as they develop into adults. These changes happen at a stage called puberty.

Puberty

As you grow up, lots of things will happen to you. They won't all happen at the same time to everyone. This is perfectly normal. As your body grows and matures and you change from being a child to an adult you go through what is called **puberty**. Puberty can be a difficult time, but it's nothing to worry about.

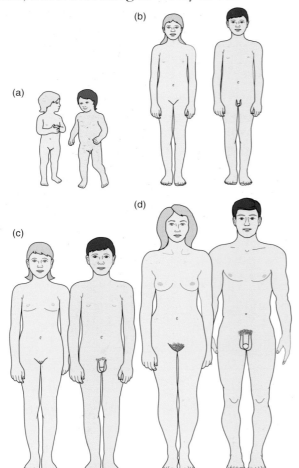

Figure 1 Some of the physical changes that take place when you grow up.

It is easy to see the physical changes that happen after you reach puberty (Figure 1). What is not so easy to see are the other changes that take place. Table 1 lists the sorts of changes that take place in boys and girls during puberty. Many of the changes are caused by **hormones**. Hormones are natural chemicals in your body that control things. Menstruation and growing body hair are caused by the presence of hormones.

Questions

1 How have you changed in the last four years?

2 What do you like and what do you not like about the changes?

3 How do you think you'll be different in five more years?

4 Do you think you'll like these changes?

5 What are the physical changes we can see in Figure 1 as we move from an adolescent to an adult?

6 What changes take place that we cannot see?

7 Exercise specialists say that young boys should not do a lot of heavy weight training before they are 16 years of age. Why do you think they give this advice?

8 Young girls often try to diet as they are going through puberty. What changes in their bodies might make young girls want to diet and why could it be harmful to them?

The menstrual cycle

Once a girl reaches adolescence, the time when she is changing from a girl to a woman, she begins to have periods. This is what we

During puberty what happens to . . .	Boys	Girls
My body size?	The whole body begins to grow faster – a growth spurt – and your shoulders will broaden. You will also begin to develop more defined muscles.	The whole body begins to grow faster – a growth spurt. You will begin to get curves as your body deposits fat on your hips, buttocks and thighs.
My hair?	The hair on your head could become greasier and you will begin to grow body hair under your arms, on your chest, on your arms and legs and around your penis (pubic hair). You will also have an increase in growth of facial hair.	The hair on your head could become greasier and you will begin to grow body hair under your arms and around your vagina (pubic hair).
My voice?	Your voice becomes deeper and your larynx (Adam's Apple) gets larger.	Your voice won't change much.
My skin?	You could develop 'spots' or mild acne. If it gets bad, see your pharmacist or doctor.	You could develop 'spots' or mild acne. If it gets bad, see your pharmacist or doctor.
My reproductive organs?	Your testes will grow larger and start producing sperm. Your penis will grow larger and may get slightly darker.	You will begin to grow breasts (mammary glands), your ovaries will begin to produce eggs and you will start to menstruate (have periods).

Table 1

commonly call **menstruation**. Once an egg is released, the womb prepares to receive it. To do this the wall of the womb thickens. The lining of the womb has a rich supply of blood vessels. If a fertilised egg does not reach the womb and attach to the lining, the body knows that the lining is not needed. It breaks down and is passed out of the body through the vagina. This process is controlled by two hormones, **progesterone** and **oestrogen**.

In young girls just reaching puberty, their period may be irregular but as they grow older it should settle down and happen once every 28–30 days. The egg is released on or around day 14. The first day of bleeding in a woman is day 1 of the period.

Girls may begin to have periods at any age from about 9–17, usually around the age of 12 or 13. Lots of things can affect exactly when a girl's period will first begin such as her diet, overall health, amount of exercise, weight and genes (see page 83).

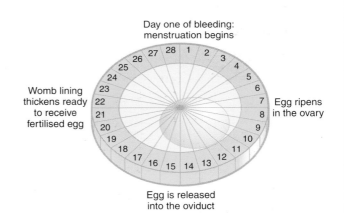

Figure 2 The menstrual cycle

> ## Remember
>
> Write a sentence to describe each of these changes at puberty:
>
> Growth spurt
> Body hair and pubic hair
> Breasts and hips
> Muscular development
> Sexual development

The problem page

Teenage magazines often have a problem page. They employ an 'agony aunt' or 'uncle' to try and solve your problems. Teenagers often moan about their parents not understanding what it is like growing up, but do remember they have also gone through what you're going through, even if it was some time ago!

Try putting yourself in the place of a parent or agony aunt/uncle. Read the teenager's problems below and try to give them good, sensible advice. You may need to think back to some of the science you've learned about what happens when you grow up in order to help or reassure them. Write your replies in the form of letters to the teenagers.

Teenage problem 1

DEAR PROBLEM PAGE
I DON'T KNOW WHAT'S GOING ON. I AM A BOY OF 12 YEARS OF AGE. THE PROBLEM IS THAT EVERY TIME I OPEN MY MOUTH, MY VOICE SEEMS TO SQUEAK. ONE MINUTE IT'S HIGH PITCHED, THE NEXT VERY LOW. IT'S DIFFICULT FOR ME TO ANSWER QUESTIONS IN CLASS BECAUSE I THINK THE OTHERS WILL MAKE FUN OF ME. CAN YOU HELP ME AND LET ME KNOW WHAT'S GOING ON?

WORRIED OF WANDSWORTH

Teenage problem 2

Dear problem page
It's just not fair! I'm 14 and I haven't had my first period yet. I must be a freak. All my friends say they've had loads. Am I really a freak? Will I ever have a period?

Depressed of Derby

Teenage problem 3

Dear problem page

My mother is pregnant and I am worried. I don't see how a baby can survive inside her. I know that we all need oxygen to live and food to help us grow, including babies! What I don't understand is how the baby will get these if it's inside my mum. Can you please explain what is going on?

Confused of Clacton

Squeek!

Figure 1

Teenage problem 4

Dear problem page
My mother keeps on at me about how often I wash my hair. The trouble is I think it is greasy. It never used to be like this and there is no way that I am going to school with hair like that. She keeps shouting at me in the morning to hurry up in the shower. It wouldn't be so bad but she takes twice as long as me. If I could only give her a reason why I take so long then it wouldn't be so bad. Can you help?

Annoyed of Andover

Teenage problem 5

Dear problem page
When I have a shower after P.E., I find it difficult because I am beginning to grow some hair under my arms and around my private parts. Is this normal? (I am 12 years of age.) I thought that only adults grew hair on their body, surely I am too young for this. My friends point and snigger but am I right that this will also happen to them?

Shy of Sheffield

Figure 3

Teenage problem 6

Dear problem page
My friends have told me that kissing and cuddling can make a girl pregnant. I'm not certain that it does. I know that fertilisation has to take place because I remember hearing something about it in my science lesson. I wasn't listening in class so I didn't hear the rest. I'm too embarrassed to go back and ask my science teacher as she will think I'm an idiot. Can you help me and explain what fertilisation is?

Dreamer of Darlington

Figure 2

Remember

Design the front page of a leaflet for unhappy people of your age. The title of the leaflet is 'Share your concerns; everybody has problems growing up'.

Finishing off!

Remember

Complete the following paragraphs using some or all of the words in bold. A word may be used more than once.

ovaries uterus puberty adolescence scrotal sacs vagina fertilisation penis placenta foetus menstruation larynx nutrition testes

When a sperm cell joins with an egg cell it is called _____**1**_____. This is the start of life. Egg cells are produced in a woman's _____**2**_____. The egg will travel down the oviduct and, if fertilised, will attach to the wall of the _____**3**_____ or womb. As the fertilised egg grows in the womb, a round disc-shaped organ called the _____**4**_____ also grows. This provides oxygen and _____**5**_____ for the growing embryo. Once individual parts can be identified, the embryo is called a _____**6**_____.

In men, sperm cells are produced in the _____**7**_____. These are found outside the body inside the _____**8**_____. They are outside the body because it is cooler – body temperature can stop sperm developing. Sperm are deposited in the _____**9**_____ during sexual intercourse. They swim into the womb and up into the oviduct where, if they meet an egg, they can join with it. This is called _____**10**_____.

At about the age of 12 most boys and girls begin to go through _____**11**_____. It can happen earlier or later, however. While we change from children to adults we go through what is called _____**12**_____. After puberty, girls start _____**13**_____ and a physical change that often happens in boys is that the _____**14**_____ in their throat gets larger.

Web sites to visit:

Kids Health – answering questions about puberty
http://kidshealth.org/kid/somebody/puberty.html

Parenthood Web – ultrasound images of foetuses
http://www.parenthood.com/parent_cfmfiles/us.clm/574

Solutions

Starter Activity
Filtering

You should know about filtering. You have seen it done lots of times to separate a liquid and a solid. Sometimes it's called straining, like when we separate peas from hot water.

Our water supply is filtered through sand to catch small particles before it is treated and sent along our water pipes. Swimming pools also have sand filters, only much smaller ones.

Operating theatre masks prevent germs from doctors' mouths getting inside the patient, but let air through.

A filter bed of sand at a sewage plant.

A dust mask in a spray booth filters the opposite way to the operating mask. It prevents tiny bits of paint from the spray getting into the lungs, but air can get through.

A colander can be used to strain peas.

Questions

1 A gardener finds lots of small stones in the earth she has sieved. How could she solve the problem?

2 Copy and fill in this table for all the photos above.

3 Filtering can be used to separate chalk and water but not salt and water. Explain why.

4 Your small sister has mixed tiny glass beads with the sugar. How could you get the beads back by using water?

Material	Substance being left in filter	Substance passing through filter

Good solutions

When a solid disappears into a liquid, a mixture called a solution is made. The solid that dissolves is called a solute and the liquid is a solvent.

Water dissolves many substances, including oxygen. Fish living in water can breathe using this oxygen. But water does not dissolve everything. If it did, rain would be a worse problem than it is.

Figure 1 This is what could happen if building materials dissolved in the rain!

When substances dissolve, the **solution** is transparent (see-through). If it is not transparent, it is not a real solution. These non-transparent liquids are called **suspensions** – they are tiny pieces of solids mixed up in a liquid.

Figure 2 Making jelly

If you want a substance like jelly to dissolve faster, use hot water and cut the jelly into small pieces. A higher temperature and a bigger surface area speed up dissolving.

Questions

1 a) Write down the names of some substances you know that dissolve in water.
   b) Next to their names, write the colour of the solution they make.

2 Make a list of drinks that are transparent. Put a heading 'solutions' above this list.

3 Make a list of drinks that are not transparent. Put 'suspensions' at the top of this list.

Concentrate on the job

Tom has a Saturday job. But he has made some silly mistakes.

'On my first day I had to make black coffee. I only know about instant coffee, but this was real coffee. I put one spoonful in the cup and added water. It turned out really weak and the coffee bits did not dissolve.

The manager told me the right way to make it. You pour boiling water on to the ground coffee. You filter the liquid that comes through. The boiling water dissolves the coffee taste out of the ground up coffee and the rest stays in the filter. You need to use a lot of ground coffee. There is less substance with the taste of coffee in it so the coffee would be less concentrated.

Figure 3 Tom in trouble at the café

I also adjusted the 'Coke' machine all wrong – too much syrup and not enough fizzy water in the mixture. People moaned about how concentrated the taste was.'

A **concentrated solution** has more **solute** (dissolved solid) in the **solvent** (liquid that does the dissolving).

very hot water is forced up the pipe and onto the ground coffee

the hot water dissolves materials from the coffee

the filter paper only lets the black coffee solution through

water is heated to boiling point

coffee

Figure 4 How a filter coffee machine works

4 Some people like 'weak' tea. How can you tell if it is weak?

5 If you make a thermos flask of instant coffee, you use much more coffee powder than you would for a mugful. Explain why.

6 Draw particle pictures of strong and weak solutions. If it was a coloured solute, how would the colours be different?

7 Devise a test to find out how much salt will dissolve in 100 cm^3 of cold water. Write step-by-step instructions.

The difference between melting and dissolving

Dissolving needs *two* substances – a solute and a solvent.
e.g.: sugar and black coffee
  tea bag and water
  nail varnish and nail varnish remover
Melting needs only *one* substance
e.g.: ice cubes in water
  butter in a frying pan
  ice cream on a hot day

Remember

Match the words with the spaces.

**solute solution concentration
hot solvent powder**

A solid ____**1**____ dissolves in a ____**2**____ to make a mixture called a ____**3**____. If the solute is a ____**4**____ or the solvent is ____**5**____ then the dissolving happens faster. The amount of solute in a solution is called the ____**6**____.

Picture solutions

Some solids will dissolve in liquids – their particles join the random jumble. A solution is formed. It does not have the same properties as a pure substance.

Flash! The photographer's shutter opens for a sixtieth of a second and the glamorous image is captured.

Figure 1

High quality photographs still use a hundred-year-old method to make the picture. The film has caught only the faintest of images on tiny crystals of a light sensitive chemical. A wet chemical process involving several **solutions** then needs to be carried out before you can view the image.

Figure 2 Mata diluting the chemicals she needs to develop her photographs.

Mata is in charge of processing the photos.

She takes the film out of the camera and 'develops' it in a solution that makes the image much darker. Mata must dilute the chemicals to the correct **concentration**. She must also make sure that the temperature of the solution is right. She has to be careful. If the image gets too dark, the picture will be ruined.

The developer is washed from the picture and the image is 'fixed'. All the light sensitive material gets **dissolved** out of the film. The film is washed again and dried, and used to make lots of prints.

The 'fixer' solution needs changing every day – not because the chemicals have been used up, but because the solution has become **saturated** with the light sensitive material out of the film.

This material contains silver and is recycled because it is expensive to buy.

Questions

1 Mata uses two solutions. What do they do?

2 Why does Mata dilute the chemicals?

3 Which solution has to be changed every day? Explain why.

4 Why is the fixer recycled?

5 **a)** What is the solute for the fixer solution?
   b) What is the solvent for the fixer solution?

6 If the developer solution is left out in an open flat dish, the volume gets less. Explain why.

7 What would that do to the strength of the solution?

8 What is a saturated solution?

9 Draw a particle picture of a saturated solution.

Complete solutions

- Dissolving takes place because the solvent particles break the forces between the particles of the solid and pull it apart.
- The solid gets dissolved layer by layer from the outside in.
- The solid gets split up into tiny particles and can't be seen.
- A concentrated solution has lots of solute particles in a certain volume. A dilute solution has few dissolved particles in a certain volume.

Key
- ⚪ Water particles
- ▨ Salt particles

Figure 3 a) The salt goes into the water. The water particles pull at the salt particles. b) The salt particles are pulled away from each other. They mix with the water. c) Eventually nearly all the salt particles are pulled away from each other. When the last ones are pulled apart, the salt disappears.

A clean answer

Sahera wanted to remove sugary marks from her best jacket. She trained as an engineer so she knew lots of science.

She knew

- hot water works better than cold as more solute dissolves in hot water.

- there is a limit to how much solid will dissolve in a certain amount of solvent. The solvent becomes saturated after a while and can't dissolve any more.
- water worked for sugar marks, but other stains needed different solvents.
- it would be a disaster to use the wrong solvent.

Sahera's cleaning tips: know the right solvent

- Use ethanol (meths) to dissolve biro.
- Use propanone to dissolve nail varnish.
- Use petrol to dissolve oily marks.
- Use xylene to dissolve chewing gum (take care).
- Use water to dissolve salty sweat marks.

Questions

10 Why did Sahera heat the water?

11 Why did Sahera keep changing the water?

12 What would Sahera use to remove biro ink marks?

13 Nail varnish remover will damage some fabrics. Write instructions for testing the fabric beforehand.

Remember

Fill in the spaces using the following words.

**solutions   dissolved   different
solute   concentration**

_____1_____ are a mixture of a _____2_____ and a solvent.

The _____3_____ is the amount of solute _____4_____ in a certain volume of solution.

Water dissolves many substances but oily materials need _____5_____ solvents.

Bends & sweets

Solids and gases both dissolve in liquids to form solutions. We are used to dissolving solids, but are perhaps less familiar with the idea of gases dissolving.

A lot of things that we see around us involve the dissolving of gases. For example:

- Steel rusts because oxygen dissolves in water.
- Fish have gills so they can breathe the dissolved oxygen from water.
- Drinks are fizzy because carbon dioxide is dissolved in them.

Deep breathing

When we breathe, air sweeps into our bodies and some of the oxygen gets absorbed through our lungs. The same volume of gas then sweeps out again.

We normally just consider the movement of oxygen and carbon dioxide. But the air we breathe in is almost 80% nitrogen, and some of this gas dissolves in our blood as well. It does not react at all inside our bodies, but just gets carried round and round by the blood.

For scuba divers the dissolved nitrogen is very important. As they dive down, the air in the divers' lungs has to be under extra pressure to enable them to breathe. The extra pressure makes more of the nitrogen from the air dissolve in their blood plasma. When they surface, the nitrogen has to come out of their blood. If they dive too deep or swim to the surface too fast, the gas comes out of their blood like bubbles in a fizzy drink when the top is undone.

This condition – bubbles of nitrogen in the bloodstream – is called the 'bends'. It is very painful and very dangerous. In the worst cases, divers can die from it.

Questions

1 "If you dive too deep or come up too quickly, your blood becomes like a shaken can of cola." Explain why this happens.

2 What effect do the bends have on a diver? Use an encyclopaedia or the Internet to find out more about the bends.

Sugar from reeds

Sugar for sweets, cakes and drinks comes mainly from a tropical reed called sugar cane. This cane grows to 6 metres in height in countries that are hot and reasonably wet. Sugar is a chemical called sucrose and sugar cane sap contains up to 15% sucrose.

Sugar was introduced to Europe in the 11th Century. In the 16th Century, sugar was considered to be a luxury – a 1 kilogram bag of sugar would have cost £10 compared to 90p today.

Sugar used to be sold as big solid lumps from cone-shaped moulds. That's how Sugar Loaf Mountain in Rio de Janeiro in Brazil got its name. Sugar used to be wrapped in blue paper to disguise its yellow colour, but it's more pure now.

Making sugar

The following steps outline how raw sugar cane is turned into sugar.

- The sugar cane is shredded and washed with hot water to make a sugar cane juice.

- Lime (calcium oxide) is added and the mixture is filtered – this gently removes some of the impurities.

- The juice is then heated in a vacuum. The water boils at a lower temperature in the vacuum. If the mixture gets too hot, it will turn to toffee – the sugar molecules are decomposed by too much heat.

- This is continued until the solution is saturated, then small crystals of sugar, like icing sugar, are added.

- Big crystals grow around the little seed crystals.

- The big crystals are then separated from the syrupy juice by a machine called a centrifuge.

- The crystals formed are 98% sucrose.

Questions

1 What plant does sugar come from?
2 What conditions does sugar need to grow?
3 Why is the cane shredded before the juice is extracted?
4 Why is hot water used?
5 Why is the sugar cane juice heated in a vacuum?
6 What happens if the sugar cane juice gets too hot? What sort of chemical change is this?

7 Why are small sugar grains added to the saturated solution? If sugar crystallises slowly, what size of crystals will you get?
8 Draw a flow chart of the sugar-making process.

Unscrambling liquids

You have learnt about filtering, but this does not separate solutions. Methods that do separate solutes from solvents include crystallising, distilling, evaporating and chromatography.

Salt from sea water

Figure 1 Sea salt extraction pans

70% of the surface of our planet is covered with water. Most of this water is undrinkable. It contains dissolved substances – mostly the material we know as table salt, but other materials as well.

Table salt is the chemical **sodium chloride**. In East Africa they make table salt from sea water. It is a two stage process. Firstly, sea water is pumped into a flat pond and left to **evaporate** in the Sun. The solution becomes more concentrated as the water evaporates. A substance called **calcium sulphate** comes out of sea water as a solid. This process is called **crystallising**. The calcium sulphate tastes nasty, so they do not want this in their table salt. Having separated out the nasty material, they pump the concentrated solution to a second pond. Here the hot Sun helps the water to evaporate so the sodium chloride crystallises out of solution. The sodium chloride (table salt) is dried in the Sun for the people to use.

Questions

1   What is the chemical name for 'table salt'?

2   What is the substance they don't want in their salt?

3   Why does this process work well in East Africa?

4   What is crystallisation?

Desalination

Figure 2   How to distil water in the lab

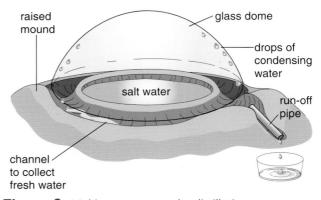

Figure 3   Making pure water by distillation.

You can 'unscramble' pure water from salt water.

The Ancient Greek Aristotle was the first person to notice this. He saw that when salt solution was boiled, the salt was left behind. The water escaped as steam. He knew that if you turned the steam back into water, it would be pure water.

In a hot dry country, a simple glass dome over a pool of salt water will make pure water (see Figure 3). The Sun evaporates the water. The vapour then condenses in the dome. A dome one metre across will produce 4.5 litres of pure water a day. This process is called **distillation**.

Figure 4 Separating the colours in ink by chromatography.

Questions

Look at the picture of the apparatus used for distilling in the laboratory (Figure 2).

5 Write step-by-step instructions to tell someone how to make pure water from sea water.

6 Why would it still work if you used dirty water for the condenser in the laboratory apparatus?

Questions

7 'Black ink is actually made from several different coloured inks.' Explain how you could try to prove this was true.

8 Explain in your own words how testing breath for alcohol is carried out.

Alcohol from breath

Inks can be separated into the different dyes from which they are made. A sample of ink is put on paper and placed in a solvent. The solvent soaks through the paper carrying the ink with it. The solvent carries the more soluble dyes up the paper faster than the less soluble ones (Figure 4). This is called **chromatography**.

Alcohol tests in police stations work in a similar way. The suspect's breath passes through a tube containing damp granules. Alcohol and other vapours dissolve differently in the granules, so they are separated. The breath then passes through a detector. This tells the police how much alcohol is in the suspect's body.

Remember

Copy the table and draw lines to make correct links.

Separation method	Description
chromatography	as the solvent evaporates, solid materials appear
distilling	boiling a liquid, then condensing the vapour
evaporating	one material carries a mixture through another
crystallising	liquid escaping from the surface of a solution

States change

Most materials can change state. Going from solid to liquid is called melting. Going from liquid to gas is called boiling or evaporating.

Breakfast! Mandy is a chocoholic. She likes to start the day with a hot chocolate drink and a piece of cake with chocolate on the top.

Melting

Figure 1

When the cook in Figure 1 melts the chocolate, it changes from being square chunks of chocolate bar to a brown liquid. It has to be heated on top of hot water for this to happen. The solid chocolate lumps change to a runny liquid.

When the chocolate is spread on the cake it solidifies as it cools. It remains in the shape it was spread into.

A 250 g bar of milk chocolate makes 250 g of melted chocolate. The weight does not get more or less when it melts but the melted chocolate has more energy.

Think about this experiment. Only the hands were used to heat the beaker.

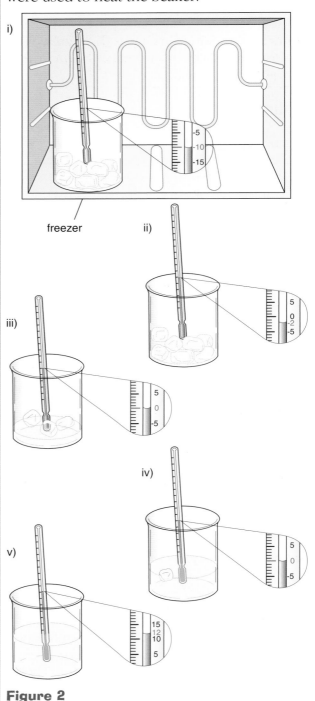

Figure 2

i) **Freezing** is the opposite of melting. If you touch ice in the freezer with a damp hand, it will get frozen onto the ice.

ii) When the ice is first in the beaker, it is dry and the temperature is below 0°C.

iii) The ice melts slowly. When the ice is melting the temperature is 0°C. The ice turns into water.

iv) The temperature stays at 0°C until all the ice has melted. Even if a tiny amount of ice is left it will be 0°C.

v) When all the ice has melted, only then does the water in the beaker begin to get warmer.

Figure 3 This is the correct way to take the temperature of boiling liquid. Don't let the thermometer touch the bottom of the beaker or the reading will be too high. Water boils at exactly **100°C**.

Questions

1 Ice tastes the same as water. Why?

2 Draw a strip cartoon of what an ice cube would look like as it melts.

3 **a)** At what temperature does ice melt?
b) At what temperature does water freeze?

4 Chocolate does not melt when you take it out of the freezer. Why?

Boiling

1 A hot chocolate drink needs hot milk. When you heat the milk in the pan it gets hotter because the hob **heats** it. The milk gains energy.

2 When it begins to boil, the milk forms lots of bubbles because the heat turns liquid milk into a gas. The gas makes the milk very frothy and it rises to the top of the pan.

3 It will spill out of the pan if you don't stop the milk being heated more. This is because the gas takes up more room than the liquid.

Questions

5 Milk makes froth when it is heated but water does not. Draw and describe what you see when water is heated.

6 If you left the water boiling for a long time what would happen? Explain your answer.

7 Above the pan of boiling milk, the steam is **condensing**. Explain what this is and why it happens.

Remember

Use the words below to complete the sentences.

**condensing   opposite
melting   evaporating**

Changing from solid to liquid is called ____1____. Changing from liquid to gas is called ____2____. Both these changes need energy.

The opposite of boiling is ____3____. The ____4____ of melting is solidifying.

Gases and boiling

When a liquid boils it becomes a very large volume of gas.

Mixtures of liquids can be separated by distillation.

Solutions do not have the same boiling point as pure liquids.

Making alcool

Figure 1 Sugar cane growing.

Figure 2 An 'Alcool' station in Brazil

In Brazil they can grow lots of sugar cane. The bright tropical Sun gives lots of energy and the sugar cane stores this. The people use some of this cane to make a fuel for motor cars. The sugar is **fermented** with yeast in big tanks, like when beer and wine are made. This turns most of the sugar into a chemical called **ethanol**. Ethanol is a fuel; it burns easily. The Brazilians give it the name 'Alcool'.

When the fermentation is finished a mixture of ethanol, water and yeast is left. This is useless as a fuel until it has been distilled. **Fractional distillation** is a process that can be used to separate a mixture of **liquids** because they all boil at different temperatures. Ethanol boils at a lower temperature than water. It vaporises first when the mixture is heated. The vapour is condensed to give a fuel that is nearly pure ethanol.

At the cold end of the scale

If you cool a gas, such as steam or candle wax vapour, it turns back into a liquid.

But you can also turn a gas into a liquid just by compressing it – squeezing it into a smaller space. The particles get pushed closer and closer together until they are touching. This is how liquid air is made.

Liquid air is a very cold mixture. The different substances can be separated by distillation because they have different boiling points. Oxygen has a boiling point of $-183°C$, argon has a boiling point of $-186°C$ and nitrogen boils at $-196°C$. Pure gases are produced by this process.

Questions

1 What is the fuel made from sugar called?

2 How is the sugar turned into this fuel?

3 What mixture needs to be separated in this process?

4 How do they get the fuel out of the mixture? Explain how the process works.

5 At what temperature does liquid oxygen boil?

6 How is it separated from nitrogen and argon?

Boiling

Liquid particles are in contact mostly because of **air pressure** pushing down on them. Remember the 'carnival' idea of liquids. If one of the people watching starts moving really quickly, they can escape out of the 'crowd' into the dancing procession.

Figure 3

To turn a liquid into a gas the **particles** need to move faster. They need to be moving fast enough to escape from the forces which keep them together. Energy makes them move faster.

You can see the steam rising from the surface of hot water as just a few water particles escape. As the temperature nears 100°C, all the particles are moving fast enough. Large holes appear in the liquid and the water boils.

Figure 4

Generally, the lighter the particle, the easier it is to make it speed up. So lightweight liquid particles boil at lower temperatures, heavier particles have a higher **boiling point**. But there are exceptions to this.

Figure 5 Raise the pressure and water boils at a higher temperature. In a pressure cooker water boils at 115°C. In hospitals the high temperature is used to sterilise equipment in a machine called an autoclave, seen here.

Figure 6 Lower the pressure and water boils at a lower temperature. High up a mountain water boils at 80°C, so you can't make good tea.

Questions

7 What is the difference between a liquid and a gas? Draw particle pictures to explain.

8 What does air do to stop a liquid turning into a gas?

9 What happens to the speed of movement of particles as they get hotter?

10 Explain the difference between evaporation and boiling.

11 Why does water boil at a higher temperature in a pressure cooker? Explain by writing about the speed of the particles.

Remember

Match the words to the spaces.

**pressure   lower   fractional distillation
fast   particles   boiling   lighter   liquids**

_____1_____ happens when the liquid _____2_____ are moving quickly. They have to be moving _____3_____ enough to overcome the push of the air _____4_____ on the liquid.

_____5_____ particles move faster, so lighter particles have a _____6_____ boiling point. Sorting _____7_____ by boiling point is called _____8_____.

CHAPTER 5

Finishing off!

See-through

It's hard to tell if a liquid is a solution or not just by looking at it. The dissolved material will have disappeared and it looks transparent (see-through). The solution may be coloured, but so are some liquids on their own. We use lots of liquids and we don't know whether or not they are solutions. You can separate a solution into its parts by evaporating the solvent and leaving the solute behind.

Varnish is made up of plastic particles dissolved in white spirit.

Fountain pen ink has blue coloured particles dissolved in water.

Nail polish has shiny plastic particles dissolved in propanone.

Food colouring has non-toxic dye particles dissolved in water.

Lemonade has citric acid particles dissolved in water.

Questions

1 Take the information above about using solutions and put it into a table with these headings

Solution	Solvent	Solute

2 Which of these solutions are used by being spread out and left to dry?

3 Where does the solvent go when the solution dries out?

4 Draw a particle picture showing a lemonade solution.

5 Explain the difference between wax cooling and solidifying and varnish drying and going solid.

6 'A bus full of friends arrives and they spread out into a crowded school playground.' Draw pictures and explain why this could be used to represent a spoonful of sugar dissolving in water.

7 Fill in this word grid using these clues.
   a) Small pieces of a liquid
   b) The solution you write with
   c) The solid that dissolves
   d) The liquid that does the dissolving
   e) A solution dries out
   f) The mixture of solid and liquid
   g) A solution for wood
   h) The meaning of transparent

Grid

```
        D _ _ _ _
        I _ _ _
        S _ _ _ _ _
        S _ _ _ _ _ _
_ _ _ _ O _ _ _ _
      _ _ L _ _ _ _
        V _ _ _ _ _ _
      _ _ E _ _ _ _ _ _
```

Web sites to visit:

SCIMEDIA – chromatography introduction
   http://www.scimedia.com/chem-ed/sep/chromato.html

Solubility Rules
   http://www.chem.vt.edu/RVGS/ACT/notes/solubility-rules.html

Water Purification by Solar Distillation
   http://www.solardome.com/SolarDome84.html

Force and motion

Starter Activity
Diving forces

It's forces all the way for a diver. When she stands on the diving board the force of gravity is pulling her downwards. But the diving board pushes upwards on her feet. The forces are in balance.

The diver moves clear of the diving board. There's no upwards force any more.

Eventually the diver hits the water. The water provides a force of resistance that slows the diver to a stop.

Questions

The Earth pulls the diver towards it. There is a force of **attraction**.

1 Name another large object that attracts with a force of gravity.

2 Magnets also exert forces. Are these forces always forces of attraction?

3 Gravity is pulling you downwards. What is holding you up?

4 What is the effect of the air on the diver as she falls?

5 What is the effect of the water on the diver?

Speed, time and distance

Speed, time and distance are quantities that are linked together in a useful pattern.

Figure 1   The police have to protect people from speeding drivers. They use radar guns to measure the speed of cars.

Figure 2   The 'speedo' on the car tells the driver the speed, instant by instant.

Remember

$$\text{Speed} = \frac{\text{Distance travelled}}{\text{Time taken}}$$

In some areas, the speed limit is 50 kilometres per hour. If a car travels at that speed for one hour then it will travel a distance of 50 kilometres. These are the quantities involved:

speed   = 50 kilometres per hour
distance   = 50 kilometres
time   = 1 hour

We can put the information into a table and add extra information. For example, if the car kept up the same speed for two hours it would go twice as far. We can show what happens at other speeds (see Table 1)

We can work out the speed of the sprinter in Figure 3 by dividing the distance by the time.
distance   = 100 metres
time   = 10 seconds
speed   = ?

Speed   = distance ÷ time
that's 100 metres divided by 10 seconds
Speed   = 100 metres ÷ 10 seconds
100 divided by 10 is 10
So the sprinter runs at 10 metres per second.
Speed   = 10 metres per second

Speed in kilometres per hour	Time in hours	Distance travelled in kilometres
40	1	40
50	1	50
120	1	120
40	2	80
50	2	100
120	2	240

Table 1

Figure 3 An Olympic sprinter

For a cheetah that travels 100 metres in 4 seconds:

distance = 100 metres
time = 4 seconds
speed = ?

To find the speed we divide the distance by the time.
Speed = distance ÷ time
that's 100 metres divided by 4 seconds
Speed = 100 metres ÷ 4 seconds
100 divided by 4 is 25
So the answer is 25 metres per second.
Speed = 25 metres per second

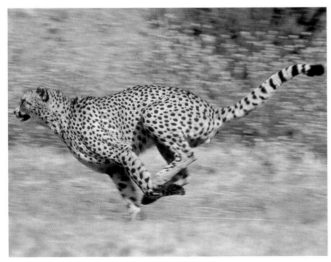

Figure 4 A cheetah

1 **a)** A car travels at a steady 60 kilometres per hour for 1 hour. How far does it go?
   b) Predict how far it can go in two hours.

2 **a)** If a runner goes at a steady 6 metres per second for 1 second, how far does she go?
   b) How far will she go in
      i) 2 seconds?
      ii) 10 seconds?
      iii) 100 seconds?

3 **a)** Make a bar chart to show the speeds of the sprinter and the cheetah.
   b) Make another bar chart to show the different times they take to travel 100 metres.
   c) Compare the two bar charts. What are the main differences?

4 Suppose that you walk 4 metres in 2 seconds. Copy and complete the following to work out what your speed would be:

   speed = distance ÷ time
   that's 4 metres divided by 2 seconds

   speed = _____ metres ÷ _____ seconds
   4 divided by 2 is 2

   so speed is _____ metres per second.

Remember

Match the words below to the spaces.

> **distance   hour   time   metres
> kilometres   seconds**

A speed limit in a town might be 50
____**1**____ per hour. On a motorway the
speed limit might be 120 kilometres per
____**2**____. Sometimes it is better to measure
speed in metres per second. Then distance is
measured in ____**3**____ and time is measured
in ____**4**____.

We can work out speed in the same way for
different moving things. We can write:

speed = ____**5**____ ÷ ____**6**____

Different kinds of force

There are different kinds of force. We can measure a force by seeing how much it stretches a spring.

Moons and magnets

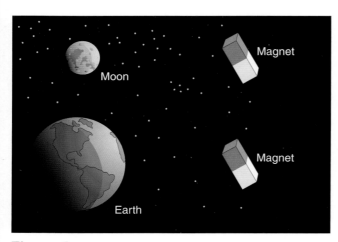

Figure 1

The force of **gravity** is a force that attracts. It acts everywhere on the Earth. It also acts above the Earth. You can still feel it if you are in a plane or the basket of a balloon. The Moon has its own pull of gravity. The Moon and the Earth are in a never-ending dance, held together by their combined gravity.

You don't have to be as big as the Moon or the Earth to feel the force of gravity. We all feel it, and it keeps us trapped on the surface of the Earth. The force of gravity acting on your body is called your **weight**.

Forces also act between two magnets. The magnets don't have to be touching each other. Magnets can repel each other. They can also attract each other like the Earth and the Moon do. But the force between magnets is not a force of gravity. It's a different kind of force – **magnetic force**.

Stretching and measuring

A force is needed to stretch a rubber band. You can provide the force with your fingers. Or you can get gravity to provide the force by hanging masses from the rubber band.

A spring also stretches. We can use the stretch of a spring to measure force. The amount of stretch is sometimes called the **extension** of the spring. We need a spring with a hook, and a **scale** for making the measurements. The scale is marked with numbers, and there is a **unit** for measuring force, called a **newton**.

Figure 2 We measure force in units called newtons using forcemeters. The bigger the force, the more the spring stretches.

One newton is about the size of force that's needed to pick up an apple. This unit is named after Sir Isaac Newton. He was the first person to say that the force that acts between the Earth and the Moon is the same kind of force that holds us all on the surface of the Earth. There is an old story that says he realised this when he was thinking about the Moon, and saw an apple fall from a tree.

Figure 4 The weight of an apple is about 1 newton

Figure 3 Isaac Newton – who realised that gravity works on apples, pears and moons

Remember

Fill in the spaces using the following words.

**newton   extension   gravity   scale
repel   weight   unit**

Magnets can attract or _____**1**_____ each other.

The force of _____**2**_____ acts between big objects like the Earth and the Moon. It also acts on objects like apples. The force of gravity acting on an apple is called its _____**3**_____.

We can measure force by measuring the _____**4**_____ of a spring. The _____**5**_____ we use for measuring force is called a _____**6**_____, after Sir Isaac Newton. A forcemeter has a _____**7**_____ which we can read to see how big the force is.

Questions

1   Which of these words describes the force of gravity pulling you towards the Earth?

friction   speed   magnetism   weight
air resistance

2   Copy and complete this table by writing 'yes' or 'no' in the spaces:

	Force of gravity	Magnetic force
Can act without touching		
Only provides forces of attraction		
Provides forces of attraction and repulsion [repelling]		

3   What would life be like if the force of gravity made the Earth repel you instead of attracting you?

Balanced and unbalanced forces

Balanced forces can keep you going at a steady speed. Unbalanced forces can make you change speed or change direction. The force of gravity acting on an object is called its weight.

Figure 1   Starting off

Figure 1: There's friction in the moving parts of the bike. But at low speed there isn't much air resistance acting against you. If you exert a big **driving force**, you'll go faster and faster. You'll **accelerate**.

Figure 2   Cruising along

Figure 2: Friction and air resistance provide forces that resist movement. There is more air resistance at high speed. But if your driving force matches the resistive forces, you'll keep going at a steady speed. You don't accelerate any more. The forces are **balanced**.

Figure 3   Easing off on the pedals – slowing down gently

Figure 3: If you make the driving force small then there's nothing to balance the friction and air resistance any more. Forces acting against your movement are bigger than the driving force. The forces are **unbalanced**. You slow down.

Figure 4   Braking

Figure 4: If you need to stop in a hurry, you can increase friction by using your brakes. Now the forces are strongly unbalanced and you slow down quickly.

Figure 5   The diver is **accelerating** towards the Earth. An accelerating object has a changing speed. You need a force to accelerate. Gravity is providing this force.

Figure 6   There is no force acting on the diver that is big enough to match gravity. The diver is experiencing an unbalanced force.

Unbalanced force produces acceleration.

Figure 7 Another name for the force of gravity acting on an object is the **weight** of the object. The diver has weight. The weightlifter has weight. The weights get their name from the force that's pulling them downwards.

Balanced forces mean no acceleration.

Figure 8 Everything accelerates towards the Earth unless there is an upwards force to balance the weight. The weightlifter has to struggle to provide an upwards force that's big enough.

Remember

Use the following words to complete the sentences.

air balanced friction accelerate unbalanced driving gravity weight

When you are moving there are forces acting against your movement. These are ____1____ and ____2____ resistance. You will slow down and stop unless you exert a ____3____ force. When the forces are ____4____ you will keep going at a steady speed. When the forces are ____5____ your speed will change. For example, if the driving force is bigger than the resistive forces then you will ____6____.

There is a force of attraction between the Earth and other objects. It is called the force of ____7____. The force of gravity acting on an object is called the ____8____ of the object.

Questions

1 **a)** On a bike, what happens to your speed when the forces acting on you are balanced?
 b) What happens when the driving force is bigger than the resistive forces?

2 Do a simple drawing of a cyclist who is starting off and accelerating. Add arrows to show
 a) force of friction
 b) force of air resistance
 c) driving force.

3 The diver accelerates to the Earth. The weightlifter's weights do not. What makes the difference?

4 **a)** Sort these situations into 'balanced force' and 'unbalanced force'.

 b) Which of the objects are changing speed?

5 These are situations with balanced forces. Copy and add arrows to show the balancing force.

Wheelchair speed

When everyday objects move, there are forces that resist their movement. To keep going at a steady speed there must be another force to balance the forces that resist.

Figure 2 Forces of air resistance are sometimes called **drag** forces. The faster you try to go through the air, the more air resistance you can feel. Drag has a slowing down effect.

Figure 1 This is Heinz Frei finishing the London marathon for parathletes. He's just travelled 42 kilometres in about 2 hours. We can work out his **average speed**.

Figure 3 When surfaces touch each other it can be hard for them to slide. It's hard for the wheel to slide against the axle that's holding it – that's friction. Forces of friction have slowing down effects.

Forces

Heinz's speed = distance travelled ÷ time. That's 42 kilometres divided by 2 hours

Heinz's speed = 42 kilometres ÷ 2 hours

42 divided by 2 is 21

So his average speed was 21 kilometres per hour.

Most of the way around the course, Heinz has to work hard to keep up a steady speed. He has to keep pushing. If he didn't, he'd soon stop. Forces of **air resistance** and **friction** are acting against his movement all the time.

Figure 4 Heinz has to keep on pushing to overcome the forces that have slowing effects. If Heinz's force matches these forces, he won't slow down. The forces will be balanced. He'll keep going at a steady speed. Heinz's forward force could be called a **driving force**.

force of air resistance

force of friction

driving force

Figure 5

The cyclist in Figure 5 has to provide a driving force to go at steady speed. Forces of air resistance and friction act against her motion. She can feel the force of air resistance. It feels like wind blowing in her face. The faster she goes, the bigger the air resistance.

Remember

Unscramble the words to complete the paragraph.

You can work out speed by dividing distance by <u>EMIT</u>. An object like a parathlete, a skier or a bus has to overcome forces of friction and air <u>NICER CASTS</u> to keep a steady speed. Force of air resistance can also be called <u>GARD</u> force. The parathlete, the skier and the bus have to provide a <u>V RIDING</u> force to make sure that all the forces are in balance.

Questions

1 A runner in a marathon race covers 42 kilometres in 3 hours. Copy this and fill in the gaps:

Runner's speed = _____ travelled ÷ time taken

that's 42 kilometres divided by _____ hours

Runner's speed = _____ kilometres ÷ _____ hours

_____ divided by 3 is 14

So the runner's average speed is _____ kilometres per hour.

2 As the cyclist speeds up, she feels more wind resistance. Draw a particle picture to show why the resistance is greater as she goes faster.

3 Explain how a yacht uses the wind to push itself through the water.

4 Copy and complete these sketches of Heinz when he is going **a)** slowly and **b)** fast. Add arrows to show the driving force Heinz must exert to overcome the forces that resist his movement.

(a) force of air resistance   force of friction

(b) force of air resistance   force of friction

SLOW   FAST

5 If you ride in a car and travel 42 kilometres in 1 hour, what is your average speed?

Floating and swimming in water

A floating object is pulled down by a force of gravity that is balanced by an upwards force provided by the water. Water exerts stronger drag forces than air does.

Figure 1   A common seal.

A fully grown seal is a large animal. It would be hard to pick one up even if you could get close enough. A seal has a lot of weight.

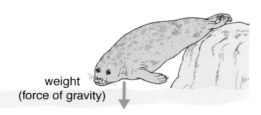

Figure 2   Weight is a downwards force. It makes objects accelerate downwards when there is no upwards force to balance it. That's what happens to a seal that dives off a rock or an iceberg.

Figure 3   When a seal is resting on a sandy beach the sand exerts an upwards force.

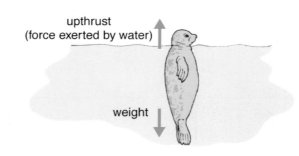

Figure 4   A seal can rest in water as well. When a seal is in water, the water provides an upwards force to balance its weight. This force exerted by the water is called **upthrust**.

All objects in water experience a force of upthrust. When upthrust balances weight, the motion of an object doesn't change. That's how it is for a seal floating on the surface.

Figure 5   If upthrust is smaller than weight, the object accelerates downwards. An anchor of a boat has a lot of weight and water can't provide enough upthrust to balance it. An anchor accelerates downwards when it's dropped underwater.

A buoy is meant to float. If you took one under water it would experience a big upthrust and it would accelerate back to the surface as soon as you let go of it.

Dolphins can swim at speeds of up to 20 metres per second. We can put data about dolphin speed into a table (see next page).

Speed in metres per second	20	20	20	20	20	20	20
Time in seconds	1	2	3	4	10	60 (1 minute)	300 (5 minutes)
Distance in metres	20	40		80		1200	

Table 1 Dolphin speed data

Figure 6 Dolphin speed

Question

1 Copy the dolphin speed table and fill in the gaps.

Dolphin force

A dolphin uses its flippers and its strong tail to push water backwards. The backwards push on the water creates a forward push on the dolphin. The forward push is the **thrust**.

Water exerts big **drag** forces. Drag is the name of the force of resistance acting on anything that moves through air or water. Dolphins need strong muscular forces to create enough thrust to balance the drag.

thrust   drag

Figure 7

Questions

2 **a)** Use the data in Table 1 to plot a graph of speed against time.
   b) Use the data in the table to plot a graph of distance against time.
   c) Are you surprised that the graphs have different shapes?
   d) If you plotted graphs like this for a boat moving across the water at 2 metres per second, what shapes do you think the graphs would have?

3 Draw sketches of:
   a) a stone that's been dropped into water.
   b) a beach ball that's been held under water and then let go.
   c) a beach ball floating on water.

   Add arrows to show the weight (downwards force) acting on each object. Add arrows to show upthrust (upwards force) acting on each object. Use different lengths of arrow to show the different sizes of the upwards and downwards forces.

Remember

Match the words to the spaces.

thrust   drag   balanced   upthrust

Any body, such as a seal, an anchor or a buoy, will accelerate upwards or downwards unless the upwards and downwards forces acting on it are _____**1**_____. An upwards force in water is called _____**2**_____.

A swimming dolphin experiences resistive forces of _____**3**_____. It can balance the force of drag by working to create a forwards force of _____**4**_____.

Finishing off!

★ We can calculate the steady **speed** of an object if we know the **distance** it moves and the time it takes. We use:

$$\text{speed} = \frac{\text{distance}}{\text{time}}$$

★ Distance moved is usually measured in **metres** or **kilometres**.

★ Time taken is usually measured in **seconds** or **hours**.

★ Speed is usually measured in **metres per second** or **kilometres per hour**.

★ **Unbalanced forces** change the speed or direction of objects.

★ **Balanced forces** produce no change in movement.

★ **Air resistance** (or drag) and **friction** provide forces that resist motion.

★ **Upthrust** is an upwards force provided by water and other liquids.

★ We measure forces in units called **newtons**.

Question

Copy and complete this table of information.

Moving object	Driving force	Forces resisting movement	Forces balanced or unbalanced	Speed – steady, increasing or decreasing	Typical speed in metres per second	Typical distance travelled in 1 second
bird flying at steady speed	force between wings and air	air resistance		steady	10	
apple falling from tree	gravity	air resistance	unbalanced		–	–
sports bag sliding across the floor	none (after it's released)	friction			–	–
ice skater sliding casually	none	none (or so small that it doesn't make any noticeable difference)				6
'plane on runway	thrust provided by engines	air resistance, friction		increasing	–	–
'plane in steady flight			balanced		150	

Web sites to visit:

Forces & Motion Project
http://teams.lacoe.edu/documentation/projects/science/motion.html

Physics Classroom
http://www.glenbrook.K12.il.us/gbssci/phys/Class/BBoard.html

CHAPTER 7

Variation and classification

Starter Activity
Triassic terrors

Biologists put plants and animals together into groups. This is called **classification**. In your primary school you probably used simple keys to help you identify common plants and animals. Keys are very useful to all sorts of scientists, not just biologists.

Chemists use keys to help them identify unknown substances, geologists use keys to help them identify rocks. The key on this page could be used by geologists to help them identify different types of animals from the triassic era, 230 million years ago. Can you name these animals using the key?

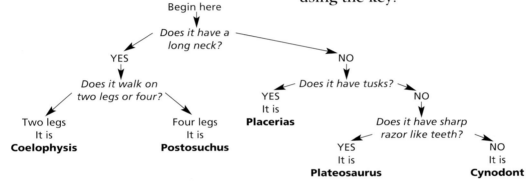

Begin here

Does it have a long neck?

YES

Does it walk on two legs or four?

Two legs
It is
Coelophysis

Four legs
It is
Postosuchus

NO

Does it have tusks?

YES
It is
Placerias

NO

Does it have sharp razor like teeth?

YES
It is
Plateosaurus

NO
It is
Cynodont

Questions

1 What types of dinosaur can you name?

2 What do you think the Earth was like at the time of the dinosaurs?

3 Why do you think the dinosaurs died out?

4 What happened to life on Earth after the dinosaurs disappeared as the dominant creatures?

Variation

All people are different. These differences can be due to the environment or the genes we inherit from our parents.

Look at the person sitting next to you. Do they look the same or are they different to you? They may be of a different sex, they may have different coloured eyes or hair, or they may be taller, shorter, bigger or smaller. They also have lots of things that are the same as you: two eyes, two ears, two arms and two legs.

When scientists look at the differences between living organisms, they are studying the **variation** between them. Some variations between living things are easy to see – for example a mouse has four legs and so does an elephant, but it is easy to spot the difference! It is also easy to see why the mouse and elephant have legs of different shapes. Other variations will be more difficult to see, such as a person's blood group.

Figure 1

Continuous and discontinuous variation

Scientists look at two different types of variation in living things – **continuous variation** and **discontinuous variation**.

In discontinuous variation, the variation must be one thing or another. For example, eyes are generally either blue or green or brown; natural hair colour is usually blond or brown or black or auburn. In continuous variation, things can have any value in a **range** of values. For example, a person's height might be anywhere between, say, 30 cm when they are born to about 2 m as an adult (quite tall!). People are *not* either 1 m or 1.5 m or 2 m tall!

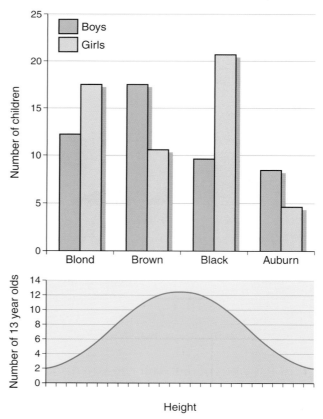

Figure 2 a) Hair colour in 13 year old children. b) Age versus height in 13 year olds

Reasons for variation

Variation in living things has different causes. Where we live and how we are brought up can cause variation, even between identical twins. If one twin overeats and happens to live in a hot country, they would end up bigger and heavier than their twin would and they may have a darker skin colour because they sunbathe a lot. This sort of variation is called **environmental variation**. In plants, environmental variation can affect how well the plants grow. There are four very important things that can affect how well a plant grows:

1 light
2 water
3 temperature
4 type of soil.

Figure 3 The family resemblance between the four members of The Corrs is obvious

If you look at your natural parents or the photograph in Figure 3, you will see that there are some characteristics or features that run in families, for example the shape of the nose, the type of hair and hair colour. This means that you will look like your natural parents or brother or sister. These are characteristics that we inherit from our parents through their **genes**. This variation is known as **inherited variation**.

Questions

1 Do a survey of your fellow class members and produce two charts like the ones in Figure 2.

2 Are your charts similar to or different from the ones in the diagram? In what ways are they similar and in what ways are they different?

3 If you could survey all the pupils in year 7, do you think your charts would be even more similar to the charts here? If not why not?

4 If your height survey was done on all of the teachers in your school, how might the shape of the chart change?

5 Many people change the colour of their hair. Sketch how this would affect your graph if there was a craze for bleached hair.

6 Would your graph from Question 5 be a scientific 'fair test'? Explain your answer.

7 Classify these variables as continuous or discontinuous variation.

- Finger length
- Foot length
- Shoe size
- Eye colour
- Arm span

8 Explain the difference between 'shoe size' and 'foot length'.

Remember

All species are different from each other, but within a certain species (like human beings) all the individuals are different as well.

There is discontinuous variation like hair colour and continuous variation such as height.

What causes variation?

Variation can be caused by differences in environment or inherited characteristics.

No two people are alike, unless they are identical twins. Even then there can be differences. Look at the identical twins in Figure 1. They look the same but one of them is slightly fatter and has a scar on her forehead, caused by an accident. Some of their features or characteristics are identical, such as their eye colour, hair colour, the shape of the nose and mouth. Other features are not, such as the scar and their weight. In the last spread we found out about environmental variation. Let's look a little further into inherited and environmental variation.

1 We all inherit some characteristics from our mother and father. Look at the characteristics in boxes below and decide which ones can be inherited, which ones can be environmental and which ones could be both inherited and environmental. Make a table in your exercise book and record your decisions.

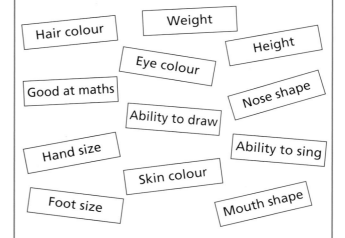

Hair colour

Weight

Height

Eye colour

Good at maths

Nose shape

Ability to draw

Hand size

Ability to sing

Skin colour

Foot size

Mouth shape

For all those characteristics you placed in both the inherited column and the environmental column explain how the characteristic could be affected by both.

Figure 1 Even identical twins can show differences.

Some people do not like some of the features that they inherit from their parents. They alter them by having plastic surgery. Would this stop their children inheriting the same features? To answer this question we can look at what we do to some of our animals. Dogs often have their tails cut off or docked, like the one in Figure 2. Many people believe that it is not necessary to dock tails. We cause this change to a dog's characteristics and we have been doing it for hundreds of years. Are dogs more likely to be born now without tails? The answer is no, otherwise we would not have to continue docking their tails!

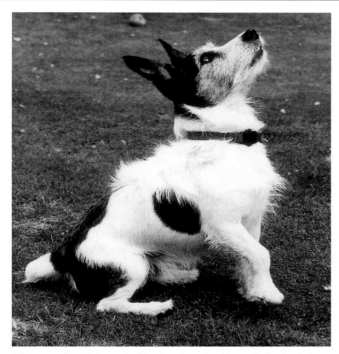

Figure 2 Although this dog has had its tail docked, it doesn't mean its puppies will be born with docked tails

Plants and animals can also have inherited and/or environmental variation. Trees growing in windy areas tend to be thinner, mammals living in colder areas tend to have thicker coats, and flowers grown in different types of soil may have the colour of the flower determined by the type of soil.

If you look at the two photos in Figure 3 you will see that although the plants are the same, the colour of the flower is not. Pink and white hydrangeas grow in soil that is chalky (alkaline), blue hydrangeas grow in soil that is acid.

Questions

2 Which of the following features do you think can be affected by the environment or the way in which someone is brought up?

Hair colour, weight, skin colour, length of the index finger.

3 A man with ears that stuck out had them pinned back using plastic surgery. He was convinced that this would stop any of his children having the same type of ears. Say if you think he is right or wrong and why.

4 Explain why identical twins separated at birth may not be identical if they meet up 30 years later. What may be the same about them and what might be different?

5 'If identical twin men married identical twin women, their children would not be identical to each other, but they could look similar.' Explain why this statement is true.

Figure 3 The colour of the hydrangea flower depends on the type of soil.

Charles Darwin

Charles Darwin was born in England in 1809. He was the son of a doctor. When he was about your age he started collecting things, and he learnt to observe carefully.

In 1831 he volunteered to sail on a survey ship, the *HMS Beagle*, which was travelling to South America. It was a scientific survey to gather animal and fossil specimens. The voyage lasted five years. For Charles Darwin it was a unique adventure and the starting point of his life as a great scientist.

When the ship found landfall, Darwin went and searched for interesting animals and plants. He filled many notebooks with thousands of observations. He made studies of living things that had not been seen elsewhere and found many unusual rocks and minerals.

On the voyage, the Galapagos Islands were of particular interest. He found some very strange animals there. There were huge lizards called iguanas, and Darwin observed no less than fourteen different varieties of finch, each with a different shape of beak. Darwin realised that the beaks of the birds had adapted to eating a certain type of food. For example, the finch species that ate insects had a different shaped beak from those that ate seeds. Darwin was such a good scientist because he noticed details like this. He closely observed things, then asked himself questions like:

- Why are some animals so similar and yet they live on islands far away from each other?
- Why are some animals in the same species slightly different from each other?
- What causes the differences?

The theory of why animals change

There was already a theory about why animals gradually change over the years. A scientist called Lamarck had proposed that some 'vital force' made animals change. He believed that giraffes have long necks because they have to stretch upwards to reach the leaves on the high trees. Lamarck said that the stretched neck of the giraffe would be passed on to its children and that this explained the gradual lengthening of the neck of the giraffe over many years.

Darwin sent samples back to Britain so that he could study them in more detail when he returned. After many years of study, he finally worked out how one kind of living thing could change slowly into another kind over a long period of time – a process called evolution. Darwin called his idea the theory of natural selection. He said that evolution happens because of the slight variation between organisms of the same species. For example, giraffes have offspring that are all slightly different. The ones with longer necks are more likely to survive than those with shorter necks because they can reach higher into the trees to eat the leaves. Because of this, it is the longer-necked giraffes which survive long enough to have children, so they will pass on their long neck to the next generation. Over the years, this lead to a gradual increase in the length of giraffe's necks.

Darwin wrote a famous book called *On the Origin of Species by Means of Natural Selection* to explain his ideas. It was a bestseller in 1859. Another famous scientist called Alfred Russel Wallace contributed nearly as much as Darwin to the development of the theory of evolution, but he is often forgotten in the shadow of the more famous man. Some of the ideas of Darwin and Wallace still cause arguments today, particularly in the USA where 'creationism' – the idea that God created the Earth as it is today – is given equal weight.

Questions

1 What was the name of the ship Darwin sailed on?

2 How long was the voyage?

3 What was the purpose of the voyage?

4 How old was Darwin when he left?

5 How old was he when he published his famous book?

6 What was the book called?

7 Explain in your own words Lamarck's theory of why animals change. Give a different example to the one in the passage.

8 Explain in your own words Darwin's theory of why animals change.

9 What questions did Darwin ask himself about wildlife he observed?

10 What is creationism?

A select group

Scientists can breed plants and animals with particular characteristics by a process called **selective breeding**.

Selective breeding

Wheat is a very important crop. All over the world it provides food for millions. The wheat that we grow today, however, is very different to the wheat grown by people thousands of years ago. Originally wheat was quite a tall plant with few grains. Today, the wheat that grows in the fields is much shorter and contains a larger number of grains. This is an example of **selective breeding**. Farmers have been selectively breeding plants and animals for thousands of years. As a result of this we have cows that produce more milk, sheep that have longer woollen fleeces, bigger tomatoes, fatter turkeys, faster race-horses and more compact cabbages.

Selective breeding is not all about food production though. Some people selectively breed living things to try and improve on them or to ensure that the breeds of cat or dog, for example, stay pure.

By taking a fast male race-horse and a mare that is also a good race-horse, breeders can mate them with each other in the hope of producing a champion horse. Dog breeders do the same; by mating dogs that have the perfect features for their breed, they hope to produce a dog that can win the best of breed category at Crufts annual dog show. In plants, breeders might use a plant that is resistant to disease to produce other varieties that are resistant to disease.

Racehorses are selectively bred. People who are involved in that sport keep very accurate records. They record how many races the father and mother of a young horse had won in their time. This is a good indicator – but does not guarantee success!

Figure 1 The Jacob sheep (left) is an ancient breed of sheep. Farmers used selective breeding on species similar to this to produce modern sheep species like the one on the right

What's new?

Rose growers are always trying to breed new varieties of roses. They select roses that have particular characteristics, such as smell, size, number of flowers or colour. They take the pollen from one rose, perhaps with a nice perfume, and place it on another rose with another feature such as large red flowers. By doing this they hope to produce a new variety of rose that has large red flowers and a nice perfume. Rose growers often name their new varieties of roses after famous people that they admire!

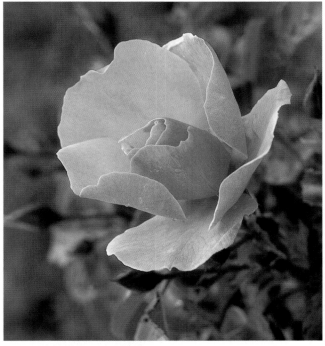

Figure 2 The Picasso rose (top) and the Queen Mother rose (bottom) were bred by selecting features of other roses and combining them

Questions

1 What advantage is there in breeding shorter varieties of wheat? (*Hint:* think about what could happen in different types of weather!)

2 Selective breeding could mean that some varieties of plants and animals may become extinct. If this happens we will lose all of their characteristics, good and bad. Why do you think it is important to preserve rare plants and animals?

3 What are the characteristics you would selectively breed into
a) a domestic dog
b) a sheep for wool
c) a pig for meat
d) an apple tree
e) a strawberry plant

4 All our cereal crops, like wheat, oats and barley, have been selectively bred from wild grasses. Explain how you think it was done.

Remember

Complete the following passage by filling in the spaces with the words in the list below.

**flower   pollen   characteristics
varieties   select   smell   colour**

For many thousands of years, farmers and breeders have been breeding new ____**1**____ of crops and animals. They ____**2**____ plants and animals that show ____**3**____ that they want and breed them with other plants and animals that have other useful characteristics. By this method new varieties are produced. Rose growers can use the ____**4**____ from one rose to fertilise another rose. This way they can produce a new variety that has some of the features of one plant and some of the other, such as ____**5**____, ____**6**____ and type of ____**7**____ .

Belonging together

Scientists identify living organisms by using similarities and differences or variations in living things to place them into groups.

Classification

Look about you at the living world. Obviously some things can be grouped together, like lions and tigers, oak trees and apple trees. But for others, like a scorpion and a house spider, it is not obvious that they come from the same family.

Non vascular plants
Mosses and liverworts
Non flowering plants
Horsetails, ferns, pine trees, club mosses
Vascular plants
Flowering plants
Monocotyledons and dicotyledons

Plants

Fungi
Mushrooms and toadstools

Protoctists
Protozoans (amoeba)
Filamentous algae (spirogyra)

Prokaryote
Bacteria, blue/green algae

Invertebrates
Non arthropods
Molluscs, worms, jellyfish and starfish
Arthropods
Insects, spiders (arachnids), myriapods (centipedes and millipedes) crustaceans
Vertebrates
Mammals, reptiles, amphibians, fish, birds

Animals

Figure 1

A good office manager will keep records and files carefully so that they can be easily found again. Scientists do the same. They group living things together in what are called **taxonomic groups** (the files). There are hundreds of groups of living things. In fact there are so many different living things that scientists cannot tell you exactly how many different types of living things there are! Their best guess is that there are between 2.5 and 10 million different living species. Scientists who study the groups and place living things in them are called **taxonomists**.

Horse evolution

It's hard to believe, but 60 million years ago the animal we know as a horse looked very unhorselike. It was about 40 cm high and had feet that spread when it walked across the marshy ground it lived on. It had to share the Earth with the last of the dinosaurs, so it had to be small, quick and nimble.

As the marshy land dried out over millions of years, the horse evolved and grew bigger and bigger. Its feet adapted to running fast on dry ground by developing a hoof on the end of one long toe bone. The larger, faster animals tended to escape from being caught, so the species evolved into the large, fast animal we know today.

Towards the end of this 60 million year period, humans appeared on the scene and domesticated some varieties of horse.

Questions

1 Give a short description of what a taxonomist studies.

2 Laura and Charles were trying to describe the differences between bats and birds. Charles said the following: 'A bird has wings and a bat has wings, therefore a bat is a bird!' Laura disagreed. She said that bats are mammals. To decide who is correct, answer the following questions.

   a) What are the main differences between bats and birds?

   b) What does a bat have that would make it similar to humans? (Humans are mammals.)

3 Put the following plants and animals into their correct taxonomic group:

   bee, garden spider, rose, rabbit, pigeon, goldfish, pine tree, crab, earthworm, carnation.

4 Explain why a domestic cat and an African lion can be put in the same taxonomic group, even though they are so different in size. Write about two other very different animals of your own choosing that you know are part of the same group.

5 One of the classes of invertebrate animals (animals without backbones) is the arthropods. These include the tarantula, the crab, the stag beetle, the scorpion, the lobster and the ladybird. Your partner, Valdet, says 'No way can these all be the same group. They're too different.'

   What evidence can you think of about these animals that would persuade Valdet that he is wrong?

Remember

In your exercise book draw a branching key to all the groups of living things in Figure 1.

The first two levels have been done for you.

Classification

All Living Things

Plants | Animals | Protoctista (Single-celled organisms) | Prokaryotes Bacteria and blue/green algae | Fungi

Clones

Clones are exact copies of another individual. Scientists have found ways of artificially cloning plants and animals.

Figure 1 Dolly the sheep – the first cloned mammal

The first known **clone** of a mammal was Dolly the sheep. Dolly was created at the Roslyn Institute in Edinburgh by taking an egg from a ewe, removing the nucleus and injecting a new nucleus from a cell of a full grown sheep. The egg then developed into an exact copy of the sheep from which the nucleus was taken.

A clone is an exact copy of another adult. Clones can occur naturally in the form of identical twins. Creating artificial clones is different. So far it has been very difficult to create full grown clones of animals, but clones of plants are very easy to make and occur everywhere. Plants can be cloned in a number of ways and some do it naturally!

Gardeners make clones when they take cuttings from plants and grow new plants from them. Strawberries have runners that grow away from the main plant and produce small plants on the end of the runners. These can take root and a new plant will grow, identical to the parent plant.

Cloning: right or wrong?

Scientists have said that it is possible to produce human clones. They also believe that it will be possible to grow human organs that can then be used as 'back-up' organs for people in case their main organs are damaged or diseased. Read the two newspaper articles reproduced opposite and decide whether or not you think that cloning of humans should be allowed.

Step 1: Take a cell from the sheep you want to clone (the donor) and grow it in a Petri dish with chemicals that stop the nucleus from working.

Step 2: Take an egg cell from a female sheep and take out the nucleus.

Step 3: Join the adult cell with the empty egg cell using an electric spark. The nucleus starts working again.

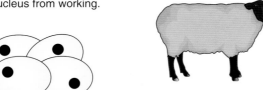

Step 4: The cell begins to grow and divide.

Step 5: The cells are transferred to the mother's womb to grow and develop as normal.

Step 6: Lambs are produced that are identical to the donor sheep.

Figure 2 How Dolly was cloned

Cloning Robin Hood's tree

Scientists have produced hundreds of tiny clones of the Major Oak in Sherwood Forest and hope to grow an exact copy of Robin Hood's favourite tree.

The famous oak is said to mark the site where Robin Hood and his Merry Men set up camp. It is at least 500 years old, making it one of Britain's oldest living trees. It stands about 80 feet high, with a 36 ft circumference, and a span of 240 ft.

Researchers at a small Leicestershire-based company, Micropropagation Services, are growing miniature versions of the tree in racks of glass honey jars.

The work is being carried out with help from the local council, which has allowed the scientists to remove small branches from the tree close to its main trunk.

These then bud and are grown in a culture; the shoots sprout clusters of miniature buds, each genetically identical to the next, and to the Major Oak itself. Each cluster can then be divided many times over.

The cloned trees, although genetically identical, will differ in appearance according to the climate and environment in which they grow.

The Major Oak is thought to be suffering from vandalism, old age and the attentions of millions of visitors. It may survive for several hundred years but the company intends to plant one of its clones next to it. The growing conditions of this tiny clone should match many of those of the original tree. 'Given 500 years and similar conditions they will look more or less the same,' Dr Neal Wright, managing director of the Leicestershire company, said.

At the moment only about five of every 100 buds survives, which makes the trees fairly expensive to produce at about £100 each.

Cloning human embryo

An American scientist has cloned a human embryo by splitting it in a test tube to create identical twins or triplets, in what is believed to be the first reported such experiment.

Dr Jerry Hall of George Washington University Medical Center, Washington DC, was attempting to find a way of creating extra embryos for couples undergoing infertility treatment.

The work raises important ethical questions.

Embryos can be frozen for many years and it would, in theory, be possible for identical people – twins or triplets – to be born years apart to the same woman or to others implanted with the cloned embryos. American ethicists have also raised the possibility of parents keeping a 'back-up' embryo in case their child died or needed an organ donation.

British scientists said yesterday that cloned embryos from a normal human embryo were unlikely to live.

Dr Marilyn Monk, of the Molecular Embryology Unit at the Institute of Child Health, London, said that even with perfect embryos, cloning was not feasible. If cells were 'split off' from a human embryo there would not be enough cells to allow the normal development of the embryo. Cows can be cloned because there are hundreds of cells present at an early stage.

Dr Monk said 'growing on' a few cloned embryos was far removed from producing a foetus. 'It would not work and I cannot see any point in doing it anyway; trying to justify it on the grounds that it would produce more embryos for infertility treatments is very poor and counter-productive, because they would be defective embryos.'

Cells are sometimes removed from an embryo for the purpose of genetic diagnosis and this work is being pursued at the Hammersmith Hospital in west London. However, any attempt at cloning embryos is illegal in Britain.

Remember

Prepare your own newspaper article giving your reasons either for or against cloning.

Finishing off!

Variation

★ Individuals in a species can vary in many ways, e.g. size, hair colour, eye colour.
★ Some characteristics are **inherited**.
★ Some characteristics are caused by the environment.
★ Individuals may look like their parents but are not identical to them.
★ Variations may be **continuous** e.g. height, or **discontinuous**, e.g. hair colour.
★ **Selective breeding** can produce plants and animals with the best/most useful characteristics.
★ Clones are offspring that are identical to their parent or another individual (e.g. an identical twin).

Classifying

★ Biologists group plants and animals according to their similarities.
★ The smallest group is called a **species**. In this group animals are very similar to each other and produce offspring that can also reproduce.
★ Two different species may produce offspring, but these will not be able to reproduce.
★ The largest group forms a **kingdom**.
★ There are five kingdoms: Plants, Animals, Fungi, Single-celled organisms (Protoctists) and Bacteria/Blue-green algae (Prokaryotes).

Questions

1 What do scientists often use to try and help them identify different types of plants and animals?

2 Put the following in the correct order:

Kingdom, Class, Phylum, Species, Order

3 What do we mean when we say that an animal is an
a) invertebrate?
b) vertebrate?

4 Which of the following animals are invertebrates and which are vertebrates?

Spider, dolphin, cat, snake, fly, crab, human being, frog, worm, centipede, locust, trout.

5 One large group of animals that no longer exists is the dinosaurs. How do we know that they were vertebrates?

6 For something to be called a species, what must it be able to do?

7 What are the five kingdoms that biologists use to group all living things?

8 Which of the following characteristics are inherited, which are affected by the environment and which could be both? (Make a table with three columns to show your answer.)

mouth shape, hair colour, height, weight, ability to roll your tongue, fixed ear lobes, ability to sing, skin colour

Web sites to visit:

New Scientist magazine report on cloning
http://www.newscientist.com/nsplus/insight/clone/clone.html

Evolution of the Horse
http://www.facethemusic.org/evolution.html

CHAPTER 8

Acids, alkalis and salts

Acid is a word everybody knows. But what is an acid?

You may have heard of 'battery acid' in car batteries and seen bottles of acid in school. These are dangerously strong acid solutions. They will have the **corrosive** warning symbol on them. But there are lots of safe acid solutions. Lemons, oranges, milk and 'sour ball' sweets all contain acids. Acids are used a lot in cooking, they add taste to food.

You may also have heard of chemicals called **alkalis**. These are the chemical opposite of acids. But beware, they can be just as dangerous as acids. Alkalis taste very nasty – just like soap.

Acids and alkalis react with each other. They cancel each other out and make new substances that are generally completely safe. These new substances are called **salts**.

Beware acids

Questions

1 Make a list of all the 'sour' tasting substances you can think of. These are all acids.

2 Adverts on TV talk about acid indigestion. What sort of chemicals are used to stop indigestion?

3 Bacteria on our teeth produce acid. What does the acid do to our teeth?

4 What happens if you mix an acid (such as vinegar) with bicarbonate of soda (baking powder)? (*Hint:* it makes scones rise.)

5 Soap is a very weak alkali. What does it feel like if you get it in your eyes?

6 Draw and learn the 'corrosive' hazard symbol.

7 Many acids are used in foods. Make a list of any food acids that you can name.

8 What substances do we use to test for acids? What do you see happen?

9 'Table salt' is the most common salt that everyone knows. Can you name *three* more salts?

10 Acids and alkalis only exist as solutions. Explain what we mean by a solution.

11 List as many meanings of the word *neutral* as you can.

12 What do you use to protect your eyes when working with hazardous chemicals?

Chemical opposites

Acids and alkalis are chemical opposites. Acids and alkalis are two different families of chemical substances. Families of chemicals have similar reactions.

All acids react with other particles in a similar way. One property that all acids have in common is that they change the colour of some chemicals. These chemicals are called **indicators**. **Litmus** is a coloured dye that comes from plants. When litmus is in pure water (neutral) it is purple. Acids change litmus to a **red** colour and alkalis make litmus **blue**. Neutral substances do not change the colour of litmus.

Beverley looked up the word 'acid' in a dictionary. It mentioned sour tasting. Beverley got lots of different substances from the kitchen and tested them with litmus paper. Her results are shown in Table 1.

Figure 1 Beverley testing for acids and alkalis

Substance tested	Colour with red litmus paper	Colour with blue litmus paper
lemon juice	did not change	red
salt	did not change	did not change
sour cream	did not change	red
soap	blue	did not change
grapefruit drink	did not change	red
cola drink	did not change	red
baking soda	blue	did not change
bottled water	did not change	did not change
tomato sauce	did not change	red
yoghurt	did not change	red

Table 1 Beverley's results

Questions

1 Make a list of the substances that turn blue litmus to red.

2 Put a tick next to them if these substances keep red litmus red.

3 Put the heading 'acids' at the top of this list.

4 Make a list of the substances that turn red litmus to blue.

5 What heading will you put at the top of this list?

6 Make a list of the two substances which are left. Put 'neutral' as your heading.

7 Why did Beverley find more acids than alkalis in her kitchen?

8 Write down the names of other sour-tasting substances.

9 Predict if they will be acid or alkaline.

Using acids

- Metal cleaner: Acid particles change the dull oxide layer on metals so it will wash off easily.

- Vitamin C: This is added to food so that its acid particles gobble up the oxygen particles that make food go off.

- Aspirin: Acid in aspirin attacks harmful particles in our blood.

A thinking model

Figure 2 Acid particles behave like these nippy mice.

Acid particles are a little bit like mice. They are little nippy particles that move about 'biting' other particles and making them change. Like mice, a few acid particles are not a problem – they can even be quite useful and nice. But when there are lots and lots they become dangerous and begin to bite everything in sight. Imagine being in a box with hundreds of hungry mice!

Using alkalis

Figure 3 These substances all contain alkalis.

Alkalis have different active particles in them. They are often used to destroy grease. Oven cleaner is a strong alkali. Alkali particles do not taste nice at all. That's why toothpaste and indigestion tablets always have a strong flavour added.

Remember

Use the following words to complete the sentences.

**litmus   neutral   opposite   alkalis
similar   chemicals   red   indicators**

Acids are a family of ____1____ . This means that all acids will do ____2____ chemical changes. Acids turn litmus ____3____ .

____4____ are the chemical ____5____ of acids. Alkalis turn ____6____ blue. Chemicals like litmus are ____7____ .

Chemicals can be neither acid or alkaline, these are ____8____ .

Measuring acids

Acid and alkali solutions are not all the same strength. The most dangerous are the concentrated solutions. The pH scale is used to measure acidity.

Less dangerous acids

citric acid – lemonade
malic acid – apples
tartaric acid – baking powder
ethanoic acid – vinegar

More dangerous laboratory acids

 Corrosive

sulphuric acid – car batteries
nitric acid – cleaning metals
hydrochloric acid – there is a weak harmless solution in the stomach

Table 1

Universal Indicator

You know from Spread 8.1 that litmus goes red with acid and blue with alkali. **Universal Indicator** is a mixture of dyes that goes different colours according to how **concentrated** the acid or alkali in a solution is.

You can buy Universal Indicator solution, or Universal Indicator paper. The paper has been soaked in the solution and dried. The paper is often sold in garden centres.

The pH scale

The **pH scale** is a special scale for measuring acidity. An electronic device can tell you the pH number directly. Or you can get the pH number by using the colour that Universal Indicator turns and matching it.

pH: 0 1 2 3 4 5 6 7 8 9 10 11 12 13 14

Figure 1 The colour range of Universal Indicator. The pH number shown by each colour is given above the tubes.

Why are acids dangerous?

Acids can be dangerous. When they dissolve in water, the acid compound splits up to make smaller particles. Some of these particles are **hydrogen ions**. They are like fierce animals – they will tear other particles apart. If the substance is acidic, these hydrogen ions are always there. There will be other particles as well – these make up the other half of the acid substance.

The 'hydrogen ion' particles react with metals and rocks to dissolve them. They will also destroy your skin and leave your flesh exposed. This is similar to how a flame burns you. So we talk about 'acid burns' even when acid is cold. Lots of acid particles are a problem but your tough leathery skin can cope with a few acid particles. They will even tickle your taste buds (like in lemonade).

Alkali substances dissolve to produce harmful particles as well – these are called **hydroxide ions**. They are just as fierce as hydrogen ions in acids. They have a harmful effect on organic matter. They will attack grease in your skin, flesh and even wood. They are called **caustic** chemicals.

Questions

Copy and complete this table for Raman. He has done acidity tests on a range of solutions. Some have been tested with Universal Indicator paper and some with a pH meter.

Solution	Reading from pH meter	Colour of Universal Indicator paper
1 black coffee	5	
2 limewater	12	
3 blood	8	
4 sea water		green
5 milk		yellow
6 ammonia solution (surface cleaner)	11	
7 oven cleaner (sodium hydroxide)		purple
8 rust remover (phosphoric acid)		red

9 How strong an acid is phosphoric acid (rust remover)?

10 How strong an alkali is sea water?

11 Name a strong alkali.

12 Name a (very) weak acid.

Figure 2 The 'savage' hydrogen and hydroxide ions.

Question

13 Copy and complete this table.

Materials harmed by acids	Materials harmed by alkalis

Remember

Match the words to the spaces.

**Universal Indicator   concentrated
solution   hydrogen   hydroxide
pH scale**

Acids contain very reactive particles called ___HYDROGEN 1___ ions. For alkalis, the particles are ___HYDROXIDE 2___ ions.

The ___PH SCALE 3___ is used to measure how concentrated the ___SOLUTION 4___ is ___UNIVERSAL 5___ ___INDICATOR___ goes different colours in different strengths of acid solution.

Acids and alkalis are at their most dangerous when the solution is ___CONCENTRATED 6___ .

Salt and water

Acids react with alkalis. The result is that water molecules get made. The other particles that are left make a new substance called a salt. There are many different sorts of salts.

acid + alkali → salt + water

Acid and alkalis come together to make new substances. The **acidic** hydrogen ions will combine with **alkaline** hydroxide ions. They join together to make **water** particles. So two dangerous particles combine to make a neutral one. This is called **neutralisation**. The other parts of the acid and alkali solution are left behind when this happens. What is left forms a chemical called a **salt**.

Figure 2 a) Equipment for making a neutral solution. b) Alkali on its own. c) Colour changes when acid added. d) Now too much acid. e) Neutral

Figure 1 Place two or three drops of acid on a petri dish or glass slide. Add the same amount of alkali. Mix with the end of the dropper and heat very gently. The water evaporates leaving crystals of salt.

Making salts

To show up the change in pH of the solution, you need an indicator or a pH meter. Make the solution exactly neutral and you will have the salt you want with no acid or alkali particles.

The coloured indicator can be removed using charcoal. Charcoal is able to absorb coloured materials. Then if you evaporate the water, crystals of salt are left.

Naming the salt

You can work out the name of the salt from the names of the acid and alkali that made it (see Table 1).

Figure 3

First part of name from alkali		Second part of name from acid
sodium hydroxide makes **'sodium'**	with	hydrochloric acid makes **'chloride'**
potassium hydroxide makes **'potassium'**	with	sulphuric acid makes **'sulphate'**
calcium hydroxide makes **'calcium'**	with	nitric acid makes **'nitrate'**
magnesium hydroxide makes **'magnesium'**	with	ethanoic acid makes **'ethanoate'**

Table 1 Naming salts

Questions

1 What are acid particles called?

2 What are alkali particles called?

3 What substance do they join together to make?

4 What happens to the other particles left over?

5 Name the salts that are made from:

   a) sulphuric acid and potassium hydroxide

   b) hydrochloric acid and calcium hydroxide

   c) ethanoic acid (vinegar) and magnesium hydroxide.

Questions

6 Is Milk of Magnesia an acid or an alkali?

7 Why does it cure heartburn?

8 Stomach acid is hydrochloric acid. What salt is made when the Milk of Magnesia cures heartburn?

9 Why does the pharmacist not use sodium hydroxide (pH of 14) to cure heartburn?

The stomach acid problem

Lucy's dad has a problem. His stomach produces too much acid. This rises up and hurts the **oesophagus** that leads from his stomach to his mouth. This is called **heartburn**.

Lucy goes to the pharmacist and gets Milk of Magnesia. Milk of Magnesia has a pH of 9. This reduces the discomfort that Lucy's dad feels. About 5 minutes after swallowing it, he feels better and the pain in his chest has gone.

Remember

Use the words below to fill in the spaces.

alkali neutralisation salt particles heartburn name water

Acid ____1____ and ____2____ particles come together to make ____3____ . The other bits left behind combine to make a ____4____ . This process is called ____5____ . The ____6____ of the salt produced depends on which acid and alkali are being used. The salt and water which are made are neutral. That's why weak alkalis help to cure ____7____ problems.

Safety with acids

Hazard symbols

Many chemicals are dangerous. They are marked with symbols that tell you how they can harm you. 'Toxic' means it will poison you.

Oxidising
These substances provide oxygen which allows other materials to burn more fiercely.

Highly flammable
These substances easily catch fire.

Toxic
These substances can cause death. They may have their effects when swallowed or breathed in or absorbed through the skin.

Harmful
These substances are similar to toxic substances but less dangerous.

Corrosive
These substances attack and destroy living tissues, including eyes and skin.

Irritant
These substances are not corrosive but can cause reddening or blistering of the skin.

Figure 1 Common hazard symbols

The strongest acid

Aqua regia is the strongest acid known. It is made by mixing one part of concentrated nitric acid with three parts of concentrated hydrochloric acid.

Aqua regia is so strong that it even dissolves gold and platinum. It can't be kept in a metal container because the metal will dissolve. It will even attack glass, so it is kept in a plastic container.

Getting pure gold from jeweller's scrap is the normal use of aqua regia. The scrap is dissolved in the aqua regia. If the acid is treated with other chemicals, the gold is separated out, leaving the more reactive metals, such as silver and brass, in the solution.

The name aqua regia means 'royal water'.

Concentrated acids

These are very dangerous. Especially as both concentrated hydrochloric acid and concentrated nitric acid give off fumes. It is safe to use very small quantities in the laboratory, but usually you would only use concentrated acids inside a fume cupboard.

Hot spot

Concentrated sulphuric acid is a heavy, oily liquid. If you try to dilute it you must be careful. When you mix it with water it transfers energy to its surroundings. The surrounding material gets hotter. This makes the liquids get very hot and boil.

The rule is to ADD ACID TO WATER. Then only a small amount of energy is released. NEVER add water to the concentrated acid.

Figure 2 This is what concentrated acid does to cloth. Think what it could do to skin!

1 Which do you think is worse: 'toxic' or 'harmful'? Explain why.

2 What is the difference between 'corrosive' and 'irritant'?

3 Why should you not store 'oxidising' and 'highly flammable' chemicals together?

4 Why are the hazard labels bright orange?

5 What is aqua regia used for?

6 Why should you add acid to water when diluting it?

7 'A lab coat is no protection against an acid spill.' Explain why this is true.

8 Draw the hazard labels and test yourself until you know them.

Staying safe

There are three important rules for working with chemicals such as acids and alkalis.

1 **Protect your eyes at all times**
It may not be your accident that causes you damage. Your eyes are by far the most easily damaged part of your body.

2 **Never lift chemicals above eye level**
And don't crouch down near benches where there are chemicals.

3 **Treat contact with the skin or eyes with lots of cold water**
Do it immediately, but don't run, as this could cause more accidents. Diluting chemicals helps to make them safe.

Safety equipment

- Safety glasses prevent splashes of acid from getting into the eyes. Goggles are even better because they fit close to the face and no liquid can dribble through.

- Strong rubber gloves and rubber aprons are used by people who work a lot with strong acids. Ordinary clothes will soak up acid and it may come into contact with the skin.

- Ordinary plastic gloves are often used when pouring out acids. The dribbles from the neck can get on to the outside of the bottle.

- Eye-wash bottles of sterile water are kept wherever acids are being used. In larger laboratories there are full immersion showers sticking out of the walls. If anyone suffers a serious acid spill, the nearest people put them under the shower and turn it full on. They may get totally soaked in cold water but the damage from the acid spill is kept to a minimum.

Figure 3 Safety equipment in use in the lab

9 What is the part of your body that is most easily damaged by chemicals?

10 How can acid dribble down the outside of bottles?

11 Write a set of instructions for using an eye-wash bottle. Check to see if you missed anything out.

Draw cartoons to illustrate the three safety rules for chemicals to someone who does not understand English very well.

IMPORTANT: Strong alkalis are just as dangerous as acids.

Finishing off!

Acid drops

Acids are very useful chemical particles. There is a pattern to their properties. All chemical changes fit into a pattern. This is what chemistry is about.

Acids are a family of similar substances. Their properties are given below.

All acids

★ taste sour.

★ neutralise alkali solutions.

★ produce salts when they are neutralised.

★ turn litmus red.

★ turn Universal Indicator orange/red.

★ attack metals.

★ give a pH reading of less than 7 (pH 7 is a neutral solution).

All of this can be explained by a thinking model. All acids dissolve and split up to produce savage reactive particles called hydrogen ions. The other particle made from the acid is a spectator in the reaction while the hydrogen ions go about their business of tearing other chemicals apart. That's why all acid reactions are the same.

Questions

Substance	Phenolphthalein indicator	Litmus indicator	Methyl orange indicator
water	colourless	purple	orange
hydrochloric acid	colourless	red	red
sodium hydroxide solution	red	blue	orange

1 **a)** Which indicator is red in an alkaline solution?

b) What colour would litmus solution be in salty water?

c) What indicator gives the clearest colour change going from acid to alkali? Explain your answer.

2 Complete these word equations.

a) Calcium hydroxide + hydrochloric acid →

b) Sodium hydroxide + sulphuric acid →

c) Magnesium + hydrochloric acid → (metal)

c) Copper carbonate + nitric acid →

Web sites to visit:

Acids, Bases, Buffers
http://www.dist214.k12.il.us/users/asanders/acid.html

Acids & Bases
http://www.bemidji.msus.edu/~chemistry/acidsgen/acidsgen.html

pH Tutorial Launch Pad
http://www.science.ubc.ca/~chem/tutorials/pH/launch.html

The pH factor
http://www.miamisci.org/ph/ph0.html

Electric circuits

A **battery** can supply **energy** to a **circuit**. There must be a loop of wire and circuit components like lamps. The loop should go from the battery and all the way back to the battery again. This makes a complete circuit.

Most circuits have **switches** to control them. We can use special symbols for batteries, switches and other components, so we don't have to be brilliant artists to draw diagrams of circuits.

Questions

1 a) Do you have any electric heaters at home?

b) Where are they?

c) Where do they get their energy from?

d) How do you control them?

2 Do you have any electric measuring instruments at home? (A clock is one kind of measuring instrument.)

3 Copy the circuit diagram from the picture above.

a) Add a label to show which part gets hot.

b) Add a label to show which part supplies energy to the circuit.

c) Add a label to show which part switches the circuit on and off.

4 Name these electrical devices.

a) transfers energy as light

b) transfers energy as sound

c) transfers energy as heat

d) transfers energy as movement.

Energy for life

Lamps and heaters transfer energy into the surroundings when they carry a current.

Figure 1 This baby is in an incubator to stay warm.

There is a heater wire in an electric **circuit** in the incubator (but not too close to the baby). An electric **current** in the heater wire makes it warm. The wire spreads the energy into the surroundings. For the baby, the wire is a life-saver.

Figure 2 The circuit in the incubator is made up of a battery, a heater wire, a switch and connecting wires.

You can make a basic life-saving circuit quite easily. All you need to get started is a battery, a heater wire, a switch and some connecting wires.

Figure 3 A simple life-saving circuit.

It's hard to do a drawing of a circuit exactly as it looks. So we use **symbols** to do simpler drawings.

Part of circuit (component)	Symbol
Battery or cell	
Switch	
Heater or resistor	

Table 1

In a real incubator circuit there will be more **components**. There might be a lamp so that you can see easily when the circuit is on.

Figure 4 A circuit with a battery, heater wire, switch, lamp and connecting wires.

Figure 5 a) To set up a circuit, take a good look at the circuit diagram

b) Collect the components together and set them out in front of you – in the same order as in the photo

c) Start at the battery and join the components together with connecting wires

d) Work your way around the circuit and back to the battery

e) It works!

Questions

1 Write down the names of these components.

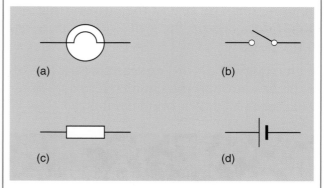

(a)　　　　　　　　　　　(b)

(c)　　　　　　　　　　　(d)

2 Draw symbols for:

a) a battery, **b)** a lamp, **c)** a circuit with a battery and a lamp.

3 Where does the energy to warm the baby in the incubator come from?

4 Which of these are designed to transfer energy:

a) a battery, **b)** a heater wire, **c)** a connecting wire?

Remember

Match the words to the spaces.

**heater　symbols　circuits　component
lamps　out　surroundings**

A battery transfers energy into a circuit. A

_____**1**_____ wire transfers energy _____**2**_____

of a circuit and into the _____**3**_____ .

There are many different kinds of _____**4**_____

that you can connect into electric

_____**5**_____ . _____**6**_____ and heater wires are

two kinds of component. When we draw

diagrams we use _____**7**_____ for the different

components.

107

Current control

You can measure the current in a circuit with an ammeter. The size of the current in a circuit depends on the types of components in the circuit.

In electricity, the word **current** means the size of the flow around the circuit. Here are some other kinds of flow around circuits.

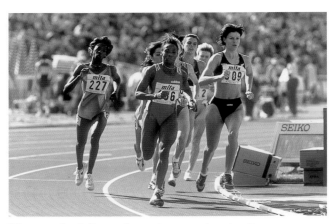

Figure 1 A flow of people around a circuit.

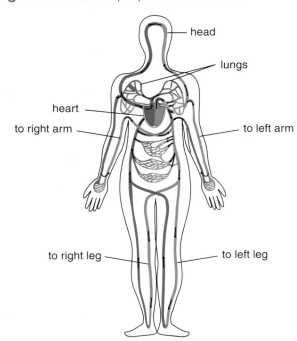

Figure 2 Inside your body there is a current of blood. Your heart is the **pump** that keeps the current going. In some places the blood flows along wide tubes. In other places the tubes are very thin. It's a complicated circuit, with lots of branches. In an electric circuit you could think of a battery as a pump. The wires are a bit like tubes or pipes.

Figure 3 The boiler, pump, pipes and radiators are components in a central heating circuit. There is a current of hot water all around the circuit. Where the pipes are narrow, there is **resistance** to the current of water.

The incubator circuit on Spread 9.1 is fairly simple. It has quite a few components but it is just a single loop. A single-loop circuit is called a **series circuit**. All the components come one after the other, like a series of TV programmes. It's more like a central heating circuit than a blood circuit.

You can use an **ammeter** to measure the current in a circuit like the incubator circuit. We measure current in **amps**.

Figure 4 An ammeter connected into a circuit.

Figure 5 A circuit with an ammeter

The ammeter goes into the circuit so that the current flows through it. The ammeter is just another component in the series circuit. The bigger the current, the further the needle moves along the numbered **scale**.

Figure 6 An ammeter scale

This ammeter scale is numbered 0 to 1.0 A. 'A' stands for amps. The **reading** on the ammeter is 0.40 A.

1 Why do you think that the current in a baby's incubator circuit must be very carefully controlled?

2 In what ways is an electric circuit like the blood circuit in your body? In what ways is it different?

3 What is the reading on these ammeters?

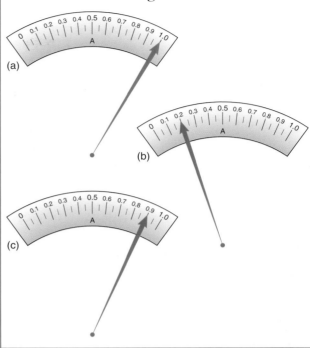

(a)

(b)

(c)

Remember

Use the following words to complete the sentences.

series reading ammeter amps pump scale resistance current

An electric circuit with a single loop is called a ____**1**____ circuit. A battery in an electric circuit acts like a ____**2**____ in a central heating circuit.

A thin pipe in a heating circuit produces ____**3**____ to the flow of the water. Wires in electric circuits also resist the current.

We can use an ____**4**____ to measure the size of the ____**5**____ in a circuit. We take a ____**6**____ from the ____**7**____ of the ammeter. The current is counted in ____**8**____.

Components and currents

We use ammeters to measure current. The size of a current depends on the components that are in the circuit.

Figure 1 There are many circuits in the instrument panel of an aeroplane.

Each of the circuits in Figure 1 has an ammeter measuring the current. The size of the current depends on what's happening in the circuit. That is, it depends on the components. It also depends on how the components are behaving. Components **resist** current. Components have **resistance**. The more resistance they have, the more difficult it is for current to flow. When a component's resistance changes, the current changes.

Figure 2 Lamps connected in series.

The number of components in a circuit also makes a difference to the current. The lamps in the circuit in Figure 2 are connected one after the other – **in series**. These two lamps **resist** current *more* strongly than just one lamp. There is *less* current in this circuit than there would be in the circuit with the same battery but only one lamp.

Figure 4 Water can go round and round a circuit – a bit like an electric current.

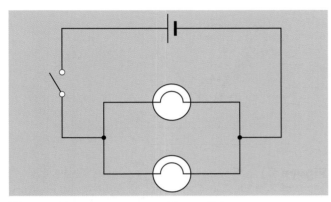

Figure 3 Lamps connected in parallel

The lamps in Figure 3 are connected side by side – **in parallel**. They both have resistance, but the current has a 'choice' of two routes through the circuit. That means that the two lamps in parallel have *less* resistance than just one lamp. There is *more* current in this circuit than there would be with the same battery and only one lamp.

It's a bit like this. . . .

It's silly to say that electricity in a circuit is exactly like a flow of water along pipes. But in some ways they are similar. A circuit of water pipes needs a pump, and a circuit of wires needs a battery. The water stays in the pipes, but if there are junctions in the circuit then some will go one way and some will go the other. The electric current stays in the wires, and it can also take different routes. The water in the circuit isn't used up, it just goes round and round. Electric current in a circuit isn't used up, it just goes round and round. Narrow pipes can resist a flow of water. Wires can resist an electric current.

Questions

1   What happens to the current if the components in a circuit change so that they resist current more?

2   What happens to the current if more lamps are added in series in a circuit?

3   What happens to the current if more lamps are added in parallel with each other?

Remember

Use the following words to complete the sentences.

> **components   series   resistance
> ammeter   resist   current   circuit
> parallel**

Lamps are examples of circuit _____**1**_____ .
The number and the type of the components in a _____**2**_____ affect the current. The current can be measured with an _____**3**_____ .

Most components _____**4**_____ current. When components are added in _____**5**_____ then the total resistance is bigger. When components are added in _____**6**_____ then the total _____**7**_____ is smaller. The bigger the resistance, the smaller the _____**8**_____ if the battery doesn't change.

Car circuits, currents and fuses

In a single loop (series) circuit, the current is the same everywhere. In a branched (parallel) circuit, the current is split into the different possible routes.

switches worked by car doors

switch next to lamp inside car

Figure 1 A circuit for the 'courtesy light' inside a car. That's the little light inside that comes on when you open the front doors. It has three switches – one in each door and one next to the light itself – so that you can also switch it on by hand when the doors are closed. Any one of the switches will switch the light on. The switches are connected **in parallel**.

Strong currents in the thin wires inside the light bulbs make the wires white hot. The wires are called **filaments**.

Figure 2 The current that flows into a lamp is the same as the current that flows out. We can show this using ammeters to measure the current. The unit that we use for measuring current is the **ampere**, or **'amp'** for short.

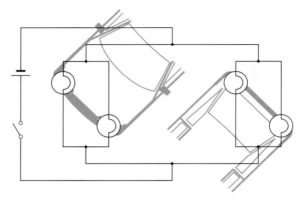

Figure 3 The circuit for a car's sidelights. There is only one switch in the circuit above, but there are four lamps – two at the front and two at the back. The lamps are connected in parallel. Each one is connected to the terminals of the battery through the switch. A large current flows through the switch when it is 'on' or 'closed'.

4 amps
1 amp
1 amp
2 amps
4 amps
2 amps

Figure 4 This circuit has the same arrangements of lamps as Figure 3. The current is split four ways and flows through the lamps. Then the currents from each lamp join back together to return to the battery. The current that goes back to the battery is exactly the same as the current that came from it.

What if the current is too big?

The filaments inside lamps get so hot that they glow brightly. If the current in the lamps of a car is too big, then the filaments could get hotter still and melt. To prevent this the car's circuit may contain a **fuse**.

A fuse is a small length of thin wire, usually inside a little tube. If the current gets too big the fuse will melt. It's still a nuisance – when the fuse melts the circuit is broken. No more current flows, and the lights go out. But the fuse is cheap and easy to replace. It would cost more to replace the lamps if their filaments melted.

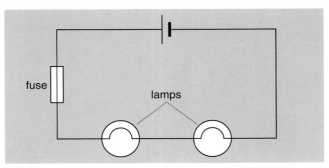

Figure 5 A circuit with a fuse to protect the lamps from a current that's too big.

4   Predict the measurements on the ammeters marked X in each of these circuits?

5   What measurement would you expect on the ammeters marked Y in each of these circuits? (The lamps are identical.)

Questions

1   What is the unit for measuring current?

2   Sketch a circuit diagram for a courtesy light which has switches connected in series. Remember that two switches are operated by the doors. What would you have to do to make the light come on?

3   **a)**   In the sidelight circuit (Figure 3), what would happen if one of the lamps stopped working?

   b)   Sketch a sidelight circuit with lamps connected in series.

   c)   If the lamps were connected in series, what would happen if one of them stopped working?

Remember

Solve the anagrams to complete the sentences.

The ampere or 'amp' is the <u>I NUT</u> for measuring current.

The current that flows from a battery is the same as the current that goes <u>K CAB</u> to the battery. When lamps are in <u>SEE SIR</u> , each one has the same current. When lamps are in <u>REAL PALL</u>, the current splits at the junction. The small wires inside the lamps are called <u>FLAT MINES</u> . A small wire that melts when the current gets too big is called a <u>SUE F</u> .

Electrical supplies

The size of a current depends on the number of cells.

Figure 1 Cells and batteries

The objects shown in Figure 1 are **cells**. In everyday language we call them **batteries**. A battery is really a number of cells working together to push current around a circuit. A battery contains cells that are usually connected in series.

In a circuit, the brightness of the lamp depends on the size of the current. A strong current can make the filament inside a lamp glow white hot. The size of the current depends on two things:

- *What's in the circuit* – for example, how many lamps, what kind of lamp and how they are connected.

- The *number and strength of the cells*.

Figure 2 A single cell and a battery of cells

Figure 3 A torch circuit

The torch in Figure 3 has one cell. It pushes a current through the lamp. The current is big enough to make the filament white hot.

Figure 4 A car battery has several cells inside it.

Cell measurements

Every cell or battery has a measurement written on it. The unit of the measurement is written as V, which stands for **volts**. A cell for a torch might be a 1.5 volt cell. A car battery has a higher **voltage** – usually 12 volts.

Electricity at home

The **mains** electricity in your home isn't driven by cells or batteries, but usually by very large generators in power stations. The voltage of the mains supply in your house is 230 volts. That's a big voltage, and it can easily produce big currents. If your body becomes part of a mains circuit then the 230 volts can drive a big current through your body. That could kill you. Mains electricity is dangerous.

When your skin is wet it has less resistance than when it is dry. That means that the mains can make an even bigger current flowing through your skin. A big current is more dangerous. That's why you won't find any sockets in your bathroom.

1 What is the difference between a battery and a cell?

2 **a)** What difference does the number of cells in a circuit usually make to the current?

b) What else affects the size of the current in a circuit?

3 Match up these lists:

230 volts   car battery
12 volts   torch cell
1.5 volts   mains electricity in homes

4 Which of these increases the current in a circuit and which decreases it?

a) Adding more lamps in series

b) Adding more lamps in parallel

c) Adding more cells in series

5 Explain why these statements are true.

a) The surface of your body has less resistance when wet.

b) Mains electricity can kill you.

Remember

Match the words to the spaces.

**dangerous   volts   cells   current
voltage   mains   battery**

A _____1_____ is a number of cells working together. The more _____2_____ that are added to a particular circuit, the more _____3_____ there will be in the circuit. We can measure the 'strength' of cells and batteries in units called _____4_____ . Then this 'strength' can be called _____5_____ . The electrical supply for lamps and sockets at home is called the _____6_____ supply. It has a high voltage and this makes it more _____7_____ than a cell or battery.

CHAPTER 9

Finishing off!

Remember

* Lamps and switches are components of **circuits**.

* In an electric circuit with a single loop all the components are connected one after the other. They are **in series**.

* In an electric circuit, components can be connected side by side. They are **in parallel**.

* Circuits can transfer energy to their surroundings by heating.

* We can use **ammeters** to measure electric current. The unit of electric current is the **amp**.

* The size of the current in a circuit depends on the number of **cells**. We can compare cells by their **voltage**. The unit of voltage is the **volt**.

* Components of circuits have **resistance**. The size of the current in a circuit also depends on the components – how many there are and what kind.

* The resistance of some components can change.

* The current leaving a battery is the same as the current returning to it. Current is not 'used up' by components.

* The **mains** electricity supply has a voltage of 230 V. It can make a big current flow. It is dangerous.

* When your skin is wet it has low resistance. A particularly big current can flow across your skin when it is wet. That is especially dangerous.

* When a big current flows through your body it can stop your heart working. This is **electrocution**.

* Big electricity supply substations and pylons carry much higher voltages than the mains. They can kill instantly.

* **Fuses** can switch a circuit off by melting. They do this when the current is too big for them.

Questions

Make a poster of a car *or* a house. Show where you will find components and switches. Show what supplies the electricity.

If you have chosen to make a poster showing a car, include a diagram of a lamp circuit that you might find in a car.

If you have chosen to make a poster showing a house, part of your poster should deal with safety issues.

Web sites to visit:

Electrical Circuit Simulations
http://webphysics.ph.msstate.edu/javamirror/Default.html#Electrical_Circuits

DC Circuits
http://www.physics.uoguelph.ca/tutorials/ohm/index.html

Science with Electric Circuits
http://www.cpo.com/CPOCatalog/EC/ec_sci.htm

CHAPTER 10

Habitats, adaptation and chains

Starter Activity
A place to live

In this chapter you will learn about the places that plants and animals live – their **habitats** – and how they are adapted to living there. We will also look at food chains and webs, what eats what and how organisms are linked together.

We live in what is called a **temperate** region (this is something you might have learned about in geography!). This means that the weather is neither tropical – hot and humid – nor polar – cold and icy. It's in between.

Questions

1 Try to list some plants and animals that you may find in the types of habitats given below. You don't need to know their scientific name; a common name will do just as well.

2 Explain how some of these animals are adapted to their habitat? Explain what 'adapted' means.

3 Write one food chain for each habitat. Remember to include a plant at the start, an animal that eats plants and an animal that eats other animals.

4 Every food chain has a big animal at its end. What do these animals have in common?

Is there life on Mars?

Living organisms can adapt successfully to different habitats.

Living organisms are found in many different habitats on Earth, but could life exist on any of the other planets in our solar system? Some scientists believe that life did exist on Mars billions of years ago. They also claim that they have evidence of life on Mars, found as fossil bacteria inside a meteorite believed to have come from Mars.

Percival Lowell (1855–1916), an astronomer, looked at Mars through a telescope and thought that he could see canals on its surface.

Figure 2 Meteorite ALH 84001

In 1984, a potato-sized lump of rock was found in the Alice Hills region of Antarctica (Figure 2). It turned out to be a meteorite that had fallen to Earth 13 000 years ago. Nobody took much notice of the rock until 1996 when tiny bubbles of trapped gases in the rock were analysed by chemists. They found that the gases were identical to the gases found in the thin atmosphere of Mars. They came to the conclusion that the meteorite was a piece of Mars that had been blasted off the surface. It travelled through space for 16 million years before it landed on Earth.

Figure 3 How the meteorite might have landed.

When the scientists looked at the Mars rock they found what looked like tiny fossilised bacteria (Figure 4). These could be the first signs of alien life! Not all scientists agree with this, but the scientists do agree that millions of years ago, Mars had more of an atmosphere than it has today and that water ran over its surface. If you look at the photo of the surface of Mars you can see the channels which water must have run through (Figure 5).

Figure 1 Mars: the red planet has a dry rocky surface but it also has a white polar cap that is a mixture of ice and dust

Figure 4 The first signs of alien life?

Figure 5 The Valles Marineris on Mars was partly formed by running water.

Lowell's mistake and overactive imagination led him to think that Mars was inhabited by intelligent beings who were capable of planet-wide engineering projects.

	Mars	Earth
diameter	6766 km	12,756 km
length of day	24.62 hours	24 hours
length of year	687 days	365.25 days
strength of gravity	3.7 N/kg	9.81 N/kg
maximum temperature	20°C	50°C
average temperature	−63°C	15°C
minimum temperature	−125°C	−80°C
Atmosphere		
nitrogen	2.7%	78%
oxygen	0.13%	21%
carbon dioxide	95.32%	0.04%
other gases	1.85%	0.96%

Table 1

Questions

1 Imagine you are a travel writer living on Mars. Write a short piece about life on the planet. Use the information in Table 1 to help you describe how life might be similar or different to living on Earth. Illustrate your article – be creative!

2 Read the following description of a Martian from H.G. Wells' *War of the Worlds*.

'They were huge, round bodies, or rather heads, about four feet in diameter; each body had in front of it a face. This face had no nostrils – indeed the Martians do not seem to have had any sense of smell – but it had a pair of very large, dark coloured eyes, and just beneath this a kind of fleshy beak. In a group around the mouth were 16 slender, almost whiplike tentacles arranged in two bunches of eight each.'

Try to draw a picture of Wells' Martian. Could this Martian really live on Earth?

3 Would a Martian be able to live comfortably on Earth? (*Hint:* think about breathing our atmosphere and what effect the Earth's gravity might have!)

Remember

Use the following words to complete the sentences.

**running water   Solar System   meteorite
little   bacteria   carbon dioxide**

Life may have existed on other planets in the

_____**1**_____ . Mars has an

atmosphere but it contains lots of ____**2**____

_____ gas, and ____**3**____ oxygen.

Channels made by _____**4**_____

can be seen on Mars. A ____**5**____ was found

which may have had fossilised ____**6**____ in

it.

Jungles, deserts and ice palaces

Living things have been found in all types of places around the world, from deep in the ice at Antarctica to the murky depths of the oceans. Living things adapt to the conditions they find themselves in.

Figure 1

Think about the animals in Figure 1 for a moment. Each of these animals is in the wrong place or **habitat** – the penguin is in the jungle, the scorpion is on the ice of Antarctica, and the gorilla is in the desert.

Questions

1 What problems would each of them have living in these places?

2 How would they have to adapt in order to survive?

Humans adapt to different habitats using technology. We inhabit a large number of places on the Earth, but there are still places where we cannot survive.

3 List some places on Earth where humans cannot survive without special clothes and equipment to help us.

4 Explain how we are able to visit those places; for example, at the top of Mount Everest, climbers need special insulating clothing and extra oxygen to survive.

Figure 2 Some different habitats in Britain

Even in Britain we have different habitats that contain different types of plants and animals which have adapted to where they live. Figure 2 shows some of these habitats.

Scientists called **ecologists** conduct surveys of habitats and list the different types of plants and animals they find there. They also study what happens to habitats when they are damaged by human activity or pollution.

The urban fox

Figure 3 An urban fox raiding a bin for food.

Foxes usually live in the countryside. They eat a wide variety of things including rabbits and other small mammals. Many foxes now live in the cities. They are called urban foxes (Figure 3). Sometimes you can hear them at night – they make a sound like a young baby screaming. This is their mating call. They live off the rubbish that humans put out and on any small mammals they can catch. The urban fox has learned to survive in the cities. People driving home late at night often see urban foxes on the roads.

Look at the two pie charts showing what foxes eat. Think about how the urban foxes have adapted their diet to living in the city.

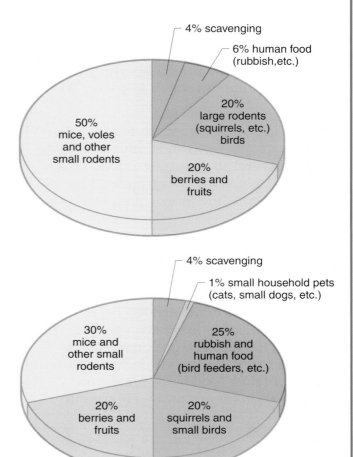

4% scavenging

6% human food (rubbish, etc.)

20% large rodents (squirrels, etc.) birds

20% berries and fruits

50% mice, voles and other small rodents

4% scavenging

1% small household pets (cats, small dogs, etc.)

25% rubbish and human food (bird feeders, etc.)

30% mice and other small rodents

20% berries and fruits

20% squirrels and small birds

Figure 4 Comparing the diets of a country fox (top) and an urban fox (bottom)

Questions

5 How many different habitats are there in the area where you live and go to school?

6 What sort of animals do you normally see around the school grounds?

7 What sort of animals do you normally see in your garden or near your home?

8 List those features that help the plants and animals live in their habitats. (An example might be that plants living on the ground in woodlands have large green leaves to gather as much light as possible from under the shade of the trees.)

9 Look at Figure 1. Describe which habitat each animal really belongs to and how it is adapted to live there.

Remember

Match the words with the spaces.

**survive   different   fox   food
humans   habitats**

All living things are adapted to the different ____1____ where they live. Animals and plants would not ____2____ if they were put in a ____3____ habitat. Some animals such as the ____4____ can adjust to small changes in habitat if the ____5____ supply is favourable. ____6____ can adapt easily to most habitats.

A year in the life of a fox

As a red fox grows up, it goes through a number of different stages as part of its life cycle.

The red fox, *Vulpes vulpes*, is found in many countries, from North and South America to Africa, Asia and all through Europe. It is a common sight in the countryside and is becoming more and more common in our towns and cities.

Foxes have adapted very well to the growth of towns and cities. Not very long ago, the British Isles was mainly farmland with only small towns. At that time, the foxes lived in the open meadowland. As more land has been built on, foxes have learnt to live among people. They no longer eat meadow creatures, such as rabbits, or steal chickens from farms. Now they get a lot of their food by scavenging in people's dustbins and around houses in towns.

Figure 1   A vixen with her cubs.

How an animal or plant lives, grows, develops and eventually dies can be summed up in what we call a **life cycle**. Read the following account of part of the life cycle of the red fox and answer the questions at the end of the spread.

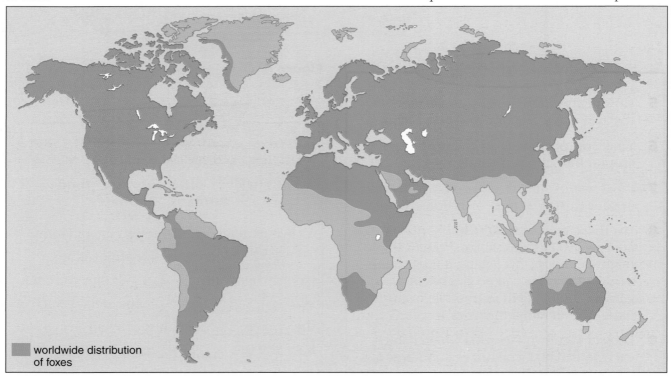

worldwide distribution of foxes

Figure 2   Worldwide distribution of foxes

Habitats, adaptation and chains

During October and November male foxes (dogs) begin to fight among themselves. They mark their territory with scent and by the beginning of the mating season, these marks will have a strong smell. A dog fox and his vixen mate will spend increasingly longer amounts of time with one another to get to know more about each other. Hunting is still a solitary activity, but even then the fox and vixen will call to each other. Red foxes usually only have one mate at a time. They are also well known for staying in the same breeding pairs for several years.

They mate in January or February. Over the following seven or eight weeks the cubs develop in the vixen's womb. Before the cubs are born, the vixen prepares one or more dens in which to give birth. The vixen decides on a den in which to give birth based on factors such as good drainage, access to food and water and how well concealed it is. A few weeks after birth, the cubs may be relocated to other dens several times. As many as 13 cubs may be born, although a typical number is five. The offspring are called cubs, kits, pups or whelps. During the first two weeks, when the mother constantly remains with them to nurse them and keep them warm, she relies on her mate for food for her and the cubs.

The cubs develop quickly. Their bluish-grey eyes are open by their second week and the mother is able to leave them for brief periods of time. By the third week, the cubs can move around and over the next 10 days they begin viciously fighting amongst themselves to establish who is boss! By week four, weaning begins – the cubs start to eat partially-digested food.

The cubs leave the den by their fourth or fifth week. When they first appear, they are a sandy, grey-brown colour. By the second month the cubs are fully weaned, and by the third month they are able to catch small prey such as insects. As summer arrives, the grey coat has been replaced by a reddish one and their blue eyes have turned to a golden colour. At six months, a young red fox is fully grown and has most of the skills it needs to survive.

Questions

1 Draw a time line to show what happens during the life cycle of the red fox. Include as much information as you can about what happens when from the passage above.

2 Where are red foxes found in the world?

3 Why do you think adult male foxes fight during October/November and how do cubs prepare for this as they grow up?

4 What advantage is there in being a solitary hunter?

5 Why might a vixen prepare more than one den in which to give birth?

6 What advantage is there in moving dens after the cubs are born?

7 Why might a young cub's coat colour be different from that of an adult?

8 How have foxes' lives changed since towns got built up?

9 Where do foxes look for food for their cubs now?

10 Are foxes a pest or not? Explain your answer.

Remember

Use the following words to complete the sentences.

survive together environment supply adapt winter mate food spring

Animals have to _____1_____ to changes in the weather and _____2_____ . All animals _____3_____ and produce young when there is a good _____4_____ of food. This is in the _____5_____ season. Often they work _____6_____ to gather _____7_____ and rear their young. The young must be able to _____8_____ on their own before _____9_____ comes.

123

Food chains and webs

Food chains and webs show us how energy is transferred from one living organism to another.

Figure 1 A simple food chain

Very few animals eat only one type of food. Most animals, including humans, eat lots of different foods. Many **food chains** can be linked together forming **food webs**.

Stop and think!

The panda only eats bamboo and the koala will only eat eucalyptus leaves.

Why do nearly all other animals eat more than one type of food?

What problems could there be in only eating one food type?

Making food chains and webs is quite a recent idea. In the 1920s Charles Elton, a biologist, was looking at how plants and animals lived and survived in the arctic, at a place called Bear Island. There were few plants and animals for him to study, making it easier for him to see how they lived and fed on each other. He found that the biggest animal, the arctic fox, ate smaller birds, which in turn ate insects that fed off leaves. The plants produced their own food by photosynthesis. He called his description a food chain.

Figure 2 The food chain studied by Elton on Bear Island. Plants → insects → sandpipers → arctic fox

What Charles Elton could see happening at Bear Island also happens in other places, although normally many more plants and animals are involved.

Step number	Name	Plant/animal type
1	**Producer** Something that makes or produces its own food.	green plants
2	**Primary consumer** Primary means first and consumer means to eat, so this level contains animals that eat plants!	insects and herbivores (animals that only eat plants)
3	**Secondary consumer** At this level the animals are usually (but not always!) larger and they will hunt other animals.	usually carnivores (animals that eat other animals) and omnivores (animals that eat both plants and animals)
4	**Decomposer** When plants and animals die, their bodies are broken down and nutrients are put back into the soil. (We don't normally include decomposers in food chains.)	fungi and bacteria

Table 1

Food webs give scientists a better idea of who eats what or whom in real life. Food webs can be very complicated, but like food chains they always start with plants that make their own food.

Figure 3 A woodland food web

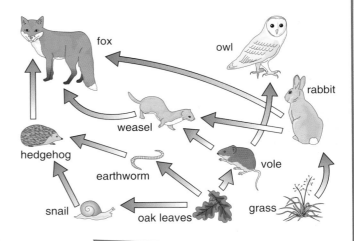

Questions

1 Plants produce or make their own food. Where do plants get the energy from to do this?

2 Look at the simple food chain in Figure 1 and the Bear Island food chain in Figure 2. Make a list of producers, primary consumers and secondary consumers from each.

3 What do the following terms mean: producer, herbivore, carnivore, omnivore?

4 Look at the food web in Figure 3. Draw a table and label the columns 'Producers', 'Primary consumers' and 'Secondary consumers'. List the plants and animals from the food web in the correct columns.

Remember

Complete the following passage:

In the 1920s Charles Elton described who ate what and whom on Bear Island. He called this a _____**1**_____ . Most animals eat more than one type of food, except panda bears that eat only ____**2**____ and koalas that only eat _____**3**_____ . Lots of food chains linked together are called a ____**4**____ _____ .

Survival!

Some animals and plants have adapted ways of helping them survive predators.

Being part of a food chain or web is dangerous unless you happen to be at the top of the chain. Many plants and animals have had to develop ways of protecting themselves from being eaten by others.

Plants have a number of ways of protecting themselves against being eaten. Some plants are poisonous, others have a bad taste or burn the mouth like chillies and peppers, others have developed to look like poisonous plants although they are not.

Animals have developed many ways of protecting themselves, from armour plating to sharp teeth and claws or camouflage or the ability to out-run other animals.

Questions

Look at the photos of predators and prey on this page. In your exercise book make a list of the animals and plants and say what they have developed either to try and protect them from being eaten or to make them more efficient at catching and eating their prey. Remember it might just be that the way they behave helps them avoid predators!

2 Meerkats

3 A bat

1 An eagle

4 A spider

5 Chillies

8 Cacti

6 A dover sole

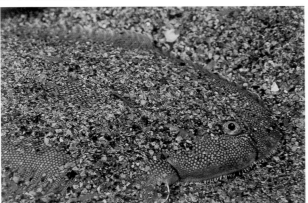

9 A snowshoe hare in summer (left) and winter (right)

7 A stick insect

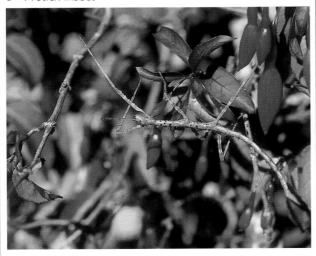

Remember

Draw pictures of these new animals:

A A mouse that curls into a tight ball covered in sharp spines when it is attacked.

B A rabbit with fur that looks just like long grass, so it can hide when hunted.

C A rodent with an excellent sense of smell but poor eyesight, for hunting at night.

D A bird with a beak and claws for opening very hard nuts.

E A deer with very big ears to hear hunters, and long legs to run fast

Finishing off!

In this chapter we've looked at plants and animals in different parts of the world and how they manage to survive. Where plants and animals are naturally found is called a habitat. A penguin's habitat is usually the cold Antarctic. They are adapted to live there by having a thick feathery coat that traps air which acts as an insulator, and by having a layer of fat to help them keep warm.

Remember

Complete the following passage using the words supplied.

**predators   habitats   cactus   primary   carnivores   photosynthesis   animals
urban fox   camouflage   spines   food web   producers**

Different ___**1**___ support different plants and ___**2**___ . In a jungle habitat, animals often have colourful markings that they use for ___**3**___ . In the desert, plants such as a ___**4**___ will have thick fleshy stems that hold a lot of water. The cactus has small, modified leaves that look like ___**5**___ . These stop water evaporating and protect the plant from ___**6**___ . Some animals can adapt to different environments, such as the ___**7**___ . It has learned to live in the city instead of its native countryside.

Plants are called ___**8**___ because they make their own food. They make sugar by a process called ___**9**___ . Animals that eat plants only are called herbivores, they are ___**10**___ consumers. Animals that eat other animals are called secondary consumers or ___**11**___ . Plants and animals are found in food chains. A food chain shows how the energy from the Sun is transferred from plants to animals and on to other animals. Lots of food chains are present in any habitat and these form a ___**12**___ .

Web sites to visit:

More about the meteorite ALH84001
http://cass.jsc.nasa.gov/pub/lpi/meteorites/The_Meteorite.html

Food chains and webs
http://www.marietta.edu/~biol/102/ecosystem.html#
Energyflowthroughtheecosystem3

Animal Adaptations
http://scrtec.org/track/tracks/t06019.html

Chemical change

Water is a very curious substance. Often materials with particles so small are gases.

- It expands when it solidifies (freezes) unlike any other liquid.
- It dissolves the biggest range of substances for any solvent.
- It passes in and out of living cells easily (try sitting in the bath too long!)

But still, it's the most common substance found on the surface of the Earth.

Our bodies are 70% water. Our life process is based on water. Our blood, our nerves, our digestion and our reproduction are all watery systems. Plants and animals cannot exist without water.

Human beings are like leather bags full of salty water and bones.

It's not a coincidence that water freezes at 0°C and boils at 100°C. It was the properties of water that were used to fix these points in our temperature scale.

Life is best suited to places where it finds land and water

Questions

1 What is solid water called?

2 What is water like above 100°C?

3 Name three substances that dissolve in water.

4 Explain simply why rain falls and where the water has come from to make rain.

5 Why does water condense on the insides of windows on a cold day?

6 What does 'condense' mean?

7 If there are lots of people in a car, why does it 'steam up' more quickly?

8 Why do we sweat and how does sweating work?

9 What is the pH of pure water?

10 Why are tap water and rain water not totally pure water?

What munches metal?

 Most metals react with acids. Hydrogen gas is produced from the acid. The metal gets dissolved and turned into a salt.

Figure 1 Alarm bells, warning sirens – you've seen it on TV. The saliva of the space monster is eating through the deck of the ship and everyone's going to . . .

Is this really true? It's usually something to do with the words **acid** and **metal**. Many metals are attacked by the hydrogen ion particles in acids. The acid dissolves the metal and **hydrogen** gas is produced from the acid. The laboratory apparatus is made of glass because acids would attack metal equipment.

But the science fiction story is not totally true. Most metals react slowly with acids and as the acid dissolves the metal, the acid gets **neutralised** itself.

after 1 second the magnesium is in the hydrochloric acid and gas is being given off

hydrochloric acid

magnesium

after 10 seconds the magnesium is considerably eaten away but is still fizzing

after 20 seconds the magnesium has gone

Figure 2 The reaction between magnesium and hydrochloric acid.

Questions

1 What happens when the magnesium is first put in the acid?

2 What happens to the solid magnesium metal in the end?

Testing a gas to see if it is hydrogen

You have to take great care. Only try this with a test tube full of the gas.

(a) thistle funnel delivery tube

conical flask

acid

metal

hydrogen

trough

water

beehive shelf

lit splint

(b)

get ready!

(c)

SQUEAKY POP!

Figure 3 a) Hydrogen is a very light gas and escapes easily.

b) Keep the gas in the test tube with a bung

c) When you test the gas with a lighted splint, it will burn with a **squeaky pop** if it is hydrogen.

magnesium + hydrochloric acid → magnesium chloride + hydrogen
(METAL)   (ACID)   (SALT)   (GAS)

A Trekkies problem

Figure 3 Baghi testing acids in the lab.

Baghi was sure that Star Trek was true and all metals would dissolve in acid. He tried four metals and two acids. He chose hydrochloric acid and sulphuric acid. He knew these were strong acids. His results are shown in Table 1.

Camel urine is a liquid that is very corrosive to aeroplanes. If aeroplanes are carrying camels, their urine will eat through the metal floor!

Metal	Hydrochloric acid	Sulphuric acid
zinc	fizzed steadily	fizzed steadily
copper	nothing happened	nothing happened
magnesium	fizzed very quickly and dissolved	fizzed very quickly and dissolved
iron	fizzed slowly	fizzed slowly

Table 1 Baghi's results

Questions

3 Do all metals get changed by acids?

4 List all the things Baghi would need to test for hydrogen.

5 Why does Baghi need to put a cork in the test tube?

6 Where does the hydrogen gas come from?

7 The magnesium disappeared. Would the zinc and iron have done the same if they were left long enough?

8 What is the name of the salt that is left when zinc reacts with sulphuric acid?

9 What is the name of the salt left when iron reacts with sulphuric acid?

Remember

Match the words to the spaces.

**react   acids   copper   hydrogen   metals
tube   squeaky pop   light**

All acids _____**1**_____ with most metals. Some metals such as _____**2**_____ are so unreactive that they do not react with _____**3**_____ .

The _____**4**_____ get dissolved and _____**5**_____ gas is produced from the acid. The test for hydrogen is it burns with a _____**6**_____

_____ .

Hydrogen is a very _____**7**_____ gas. It escapes from a test _____**8**_____ very easily.

Making a fizz

Acid plus a carbonate makes a salt plus water plus a fizz of carbon dioxide gas.

Figure 1 When the piece of marble is added to the hydrochloric acid it fizzes as carbon dioxide is released.

Marble is a beautiful stone, it is used to make statues and grand buildings. Marble is made from a chemical called **calcium carbonate**. It gets attacked by acids. Acidic particles are savage. They rip the calcium carbonate particles in the rock apart to make new substances. One of the new substances has particles that move so rapidly that it is a gas. The gas is **carbon dioxide**.

All carbonates will neutralise acids. The acidic particles rip the carbonates up, but are chemically changed when they do it. The bits left over make a **salt**. The type of salt depends on which carbonate and which acid were used.

Testing for carbon dioxide

Carbon dioxide is the fizz gas that you see when marble is added to any acid. It is colourless and it does not smell – so how can you tell it is carbon dioxide?

(a) chemical reaction
carbon dioxide
lime water

Carbon dioxide is heavier than air so it can be poured from one test tube to another

(b)

Shake the lime water and the gas together with your thumb over the end

lime water has gone milky, so we know the gas is carbon dioxide

Figure 2 Using limewater to test for carbon dioxide

calcium carbonate	+	hydrochloric acid	→	calcium chloride (SALT)	+	water	+	carbon dioxide (GAS)

Questions

1 What do you see when an acid reacts with marble?

2 What is the name of the gas given off?

3 What happens to the acid particles?

4 Many marble statues have been damaged by acid pollution. Explain why.

Put about 5 cm³ of **limewater** (calcium hydroxide solution) into a test tube. Carbon dioxide is a heavy gas so it can be poured into the test tube like in Figure 2. Put your thumb over the test tube and shake it. Carbon dioxide gas will make the limewater go white and milky. No other gas does this.

Is there a pattern?

Luis knew there was a whole range of chemical substances, all of which had names ending in '-ate' – there were carbonates, sulphates, nitrates. He tested some of them with acid. He asked his teacher first, who told him it was safe so long as he wore goggles on his eyes. His results are shown in Table 1.

Figure 3 Working with acids – wear **goggles** and **be careful**

Substance	What he saw when he added acid	Result of test with limewater
magnesium carbonate	fizz of gas and substance dissolved	limewater turned milky
magnesium sulphate	substance dissolved	no effect
iron carbonate (brown)	fizz of gas and substance dissolved	limewater turned milky
iron nitrate	substance dissolved	no effect
copper carbonate	fizz of gas and substance dissolved	limewater turned milky
copper nitrate	substance dissolved	no effect
sodium carbonate	fizz of gas and substance dissolved	limewater turned milky
sodium sulphate	substance dissolved	no effect

Table 1 Luis' results

Questions

5 Make a list of what you need to do these tests.

6 Write a step-by-step method for doing the tests.

7 How do you test a gas to see if it is carbon dioxide?

8 How many of the substances were carbonates?

9 How many of the substances gave off carbon dioxide?

10 Were they the same ones?

Remember

Fill the missing answers into the word grid and find the hidden word.

Limewater goes _____
Carbonates react with _____
Using acid, you must be _____
The fizz substances are _____
Use _____ water in the test
Put the limewater in a _____ tube

Word grid

A nice change

Some materials melt or boil when heated. Others change permanently – these are chemical changes.

Pancakes

Figure 1 In the café Mandy is making pancakes

1 Mandy mixes the egg, flour and milk until creamy smooth. She then adds salt to taste.

2 She melts a little fat into a hot pan.

3 She pours in about 40 cm³ of the mixture and cooks it for about 30 seconds on each side.

Mandy can see different changes take place as she makes the pancakes.

- When she heats the fat it loses its shape and turns into a liquid.

- When she cooks the pancake mix, it turns from a liquid to a solid and keeps its shape.

These are two different types of **change**.

When fat is heated it **melts**. When it cools again it **solidifies**. This can happen over and over again. The solid fat is able to change into a liquid when it is hot and change back again when it cools. This is called a **physical change**.

But when pancake mix is heated, the liquid turns into a solid shape. When it cools, it stays permanently in this shape. This is an example of a **chemical change**.

The pancake mixture has been heated to change it into something nicer to eat.

Cooking changes

Lots of chemical changes happen in cooking.

Figure 2 Sugar is heated to make caramel toffee.

Figure 3 Bread is grilled to make toast.

Figure 4 Egg is cooked and goes solid.

Questions

In your answers try to use scientific words like solid or liquid, cloudy or clear.

1 a) Describe what you see when cooking fat is solid.

b) What does it look like when it is liquid?

2 a) Describe what pancake mix looks like before it is cooked.

b) What does it look like after it is cooked? (Use the same words as before.)

3 a) Think of three other cooking changes. Describe what the food looks like before and after cooking.

b) Has the food changed permanently?

Questions

4 Copy the diagram of the water cycle. Label it and colour it in.

5 What makes the water evaporate from the sea?

6 Why does the water vapour become snow?

7 Does the rain contain salt? Explain your answer.

8 Why does 'global warming' make the weather wetter?

Remember

Match the words to the spaces.

melt   substance   cooking   chemical change   physical

When we heat substances they can _____**1**_____ . If they just _____**2**_____ or evaporate, this is a _____**3**_____ change.

But sometimes the substance changes into a different _____**4**_____ . This is a _____**5**_____ change. _____**6**_____ causes chemical changes.

The water cycle

The **water cycle** is about how the water in our environment makes rain, lakes and seas. There are lots of 'physical changes' involved in this cycle.

The water becomes solid (ice), liquid (water) and gas (water vapour) but it never stops being the same substance.

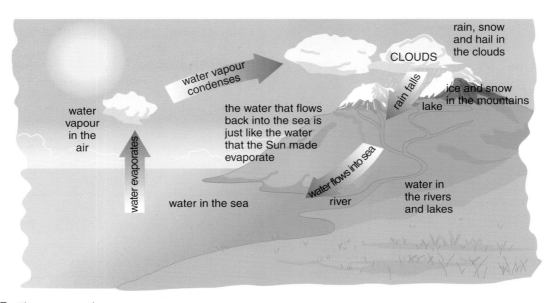

Figure 5 The water cycle

Fire

When many substances react with oxygen in the air, they transfer energy as heat and light. This is called burning.

Fire has been our friend for over 400 000 years. Fire kept us warm. It frightened away wild animals.

Fire is a fuel reacting with oxygen in the air. The flames you can see are gases from the fuel mixing and reacting with the air. When they do this you get lots of heat. This is called an **oxidation reaction**. Oxygen combines with the fuel to make new substances. These are called **oxides**. Some oxides glow white hot in the flames, making the flames their yellow colour. A yellow Bunsen flame has soot in it. The soot glows white hot.

Figure 1 White fumes are produced when you strike a match

We start fires with matches. Matches contain phosphorus. Phosphorus is an element which is 'greedy' for oxygen. A German soldier named Hening Brand discovered phosphorus in 1669. He was evaporating urine to discover a way of making gold! When you strike a match the phosphorus burns rapidly. The white fumes and smell are phosphorus oxide. The phosphorus has been oxidised. Phosphorus oxide is acidic. It makes you cough if you breathe it in.

Questions

1 What other substance is needed for a fuel to burn?

2 What is happening when you see flames?

3 What makes a Bunsen flame yellow sometimes?

4 What burns when matches are struck?

5 What substance is the smell of matches?

6 Write a word equation for burning matches.

7 Matches don't burn unless they get a bit of energy to start the reaction. Explain how this happens.

Where does the energy come from?

Fuels are made of molecules. The atoms that make up these molecules react with oxygen. The new molecules made in the chemical change contain less stored energy than the fuel molecules. This is because some energy is released. Normally it is released by heating but it could also be released as electricity or light.

Equations

This is a word equation for the reaction at a Bunsen flame.

methane + oxygen →
carbon dioxide + water vapour

This is the formula equation for the same reaction.

$$CH_4 + 2O_2 \rightarrow CO_2 + 2H_2O$$

The fuel we use as bottled gas is called **propane**. It is made of simple molecules containing three carbon atoms and eight hydrogen atoms. It needs five molecules of oxygen to 'burn' one molecule of methane.

plus

Figure 4   A propane gas burner

Figure 2   Propane reacts with oxygen . . .

When the propane and oxygen have reacted (burnt) the atoms change partners and make new molecules. They make carbon dioxide and water molecules.

plus

Figure 3   . . . to produce carbon dioxide and water

Exactly the same atoms are there. They have just swapped round to make **bonds** with new partners. Each of these bonds has an 'energy' value. The energy value of the bonds in carbon dioxide and water molecules adds up to less than the value of the bonds in propane and oxygen.

Questions

8   Copy and fill in this table using information from Figures 4 and 5.

Type of atom	Number of atoms before reaction (Figure 4)	Number of atoms after reaction (Figure 5)
carbon		
hydrogen		
oxygen		

9   What is the formula for propane?

10   What is the formula of an oxygen molecule?

11   Write a word equation for the propane/oxygen reaction and underneath write a formula equation for the reaction.

Remember

Read, copy and learn.

Chemical changes usually result in the transfer of energy.
Taking molecules apart takes in energy.
Putting molecules together gives out energy.
Fuels transfer energy as heat and light when they burn.

Burning hot

Burning fuels transfer energy by heating and lighting the surroundings.

Figure 1 Burning fuels to release energy.

Fuels

Fuels like coal, oil and gas are substances that release energy when we burn them. We must make sure we do this in a controlled, safe way. Different fuels are often burned in different ways. For example wood can be burned on an open fire, but petrol is usually burned inside a car engine.

When fuels burn they use up oxygen and form new substances. The substances produced depend on the elements in the fuel. At the same time energy is released into the surroundings. For example when natural gas is burned in air on a gas hob, the energy released is used to cook our food.

Fuels like coal, gas and oil are **fossil fuels**. They are found in rocks underground. They were made over millions of years from the remains of dead animals and plants. Because new substances are made, this is a **chemical change**.

fossil fuel + oxygen → carbon dioxide + water + energy transfer

Reactions like this, where energy is released from fuels, are called **combustion** reactions.

Questions

1 Make a list of three fuels that are used

   a) at home

   b) in cars

   c) in industry.

2 What gas from the air is used in burning fuels?

3 What is made of the energy released

   a) when petrol is burned in car engines?

   b) when fuel is burned in a space rocket?

4 Where did fossil fuels come from?

5 What new substances are made when a fossil fuel burns?

6 Which fossil fuel does a Bunsen burner burn?

Fighting fire

Figure 2 A pan on fire in the kitchen.

Figure 3 A house on fire

Figure 4 Forest fire in Indonesia, South-east Asia

Home fires kill about 500 people a year in Britain. Most of these fires begin accidentally, but how does it happen? You can get barbecue charcoal that is easy to light in supermarkets. But it doesn't go up in flames in the store. Forests take many years to grow and yet every so often you read about forest fires.

A fire needs three things to get it going:

- fuel
- oxygen
- a high temperature

These are often shown as the fire triangle.

Figure 5 To keep a fire going steady you need all three things shown on the legs of the tripod

Figure 6 To put a fire out you have to take away any one of the sides and the fire collapses. For example, to put out a chip pan fire, the fire fighter puts a fire blanket over it. This stops the supply of oxygen and the fire goes out.

Remember

Copy and learn this text. Draw a picture to show what it means.

'Burning fuels release energy. At the same time new waste substances are made. Oxygen is used up when fuels burn, and carbon dioxide and water are produced. This type of chemical reaction is called combustion.

To start a fire you need fuel, oxygen and a high temperature. One of these must be removed to put out a fire started by accident.'

Questions

Copy the table. Match the collapsed fire triangles to these ideas for fire fighting.

Method to stop fire	How does the fire triangle collapse?
7 Pour water on a charcoal barbecue	
8 Cut down the trees in the path of a forest fire	The fire stops because it runs out of fuel
9 Turn off the gas if there is an accident in the laboratory	
10 For a person whose clothes are on fire, wrap them in a blanket or large coat	

Finishing off!

★ There are millions of different **materials** in the world. You use them all differently because they all have different **properties**.

★ Many materials change state when heated. They turn from **solid** to **liquid** (melting) or from liquid to **gas** (boiling). These are called **physical changes** because the material does not change into a different substance.

★ The **water cycle** involves physical changes. Water gets changed into vapour, then rain, then sometimes snow and ice, then back to water again.

★ Other materials change **permanently** when heated. Food changes into a different chemical after it is cooked. This makes it easier to digest. Cooking is an example of **chemical change**.

★ Scientists try to use materials better by changing them. We use fuels by burning them with oxygen to transfer energy by heating and by light. This chemical change is called **combustion**.

★ Many of our fuels are **fossil fuels** such as coal. They are found underground. They were formed millions of years ago from the remains of plants and animals that lived then.

★ When a fire starts in an uncontrolled way, you have to remove its source of heating, its fuel or its oxygen to make it go out.

Questions

1 What are the three states of matter?

2 What do you see when a material is melting?

3 How can you tell if a liquid is boiling?

4 Explain what happens in the water cycle. Draw a quick diagram.

5 Why is food changed in cooking?

6 What type of change happens to food when it is cooked?

7 What is combustion?

8 Name three fossil fuels.

9 Explain why there are three ways to put out any fire.

Web sites to visit:

Handling Hydrogen Safely
   http://www.Hcorp.com/nha/hhs_2/htm

Center for the Study of Carbon Dioxide and Global Change
   http:/www.co2science.org

The Solar System

Starter Activity
Sunlight

The Sun is our natural source of light. When the Sun sets it goes dark. We then have to use artificial lighting if we want to see anything.

The Sun is very big but it is a long way from Earth. If there was a non-stop motorway to the Sun, it would take you more than 100 years to get there. The light from the Sun takes about 8 minutes to reach the Earth. Light travels at high speed!

The Sun is the source of nearly all our energy. Our food is produced by plants absorbing sunlight energy. This energy is captured by photosynthesis.

Questions

1 Imagine that you spend a long afternoon in the park. Late in the afternoon you find yourself in the shadow of a tree, even though you've stayed in the same place in the park all day.

a) What happens to the height of the Sun in the sky as the afternoon goes by?

b) What happens to the lengths of the shadows as the afternoon goes by and it becomes evening.

c) What happens to the position of the Sun in the sky as the afternoon goes by?

d) What happens to the position of the shadows?

2 You see the Sun go down at 8.20 in the evening. What time did the light that you see leave the Sun?

3 What would happen to us if the Sun stopped shining?

Sunshine and shadows

The Sun is the source of light that gives us daylight. Light travels out in all directions in straight lines from the Sun, and some of it reaches the Earth.

Figure 1 People make shadows

It is early on a summer evening. People are still enjoying the warmth, but the Sun is low down in the sky. Light can't travel through the people. It can't travel around them, either. The people block the sunlight and make shadows on the ground. We can make diagrams to show the straight pathways of light. The pathways are called **rays**.

Figure 2

Moonshadows

Figure 3 Shadows of the Earth and Moon

The Sun shines its brilliant light on the Earth and the Moon. The Earth and the Moon make huge shadows. An astronaut going around the Earth goes in and out of its shadow.

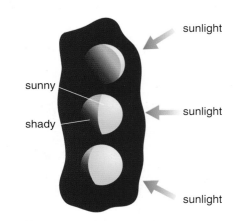

Figure 4 Sunlight shining on the Moon

Sunlight can only shine on half of the Moon at a time. So half of the Moon is in its own shadow. From Earth we see the sunny part. Sometimes we see all of the sunny side of the Moon and then we call it a **Full Moon**. Sometimes we see the shady side of the Moon, and perhaps just a thin slice of the sunny side. Then we call it a **New Moon**. The time from one New Moon to the next one is just less than a month.

Mountains on Earth have shadows

High mountains and deep craters on the Moon have shadows

Figure 5

There are mountains on the Earth and on the Moon. The mountains make shadows. With a telescope you can see the shadows of the mountains on the Moon.

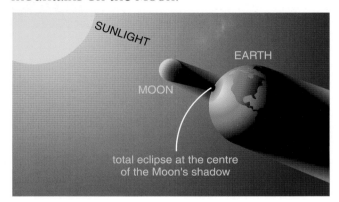

SUNLIGHT

EARTH

MOON

total eclipse at the centre of the Moon's shadow

Figure 6

Sometimes the shadow of the Moon falls onto the Earth. It doesn't happen very often. It's called a solar **eclipse**.

Figure 7 The 1999 solar eclipse.

In 1999 the Sun, the Moon and the Earth lined up (see Figure 7). Part of the Earth was in the shadow of the Moon. For a short time it went dark in the middle of the day.

Questions

1 Copy this sketch and add rays to show how the shadow is made.

—screen

2 Copy these sketches and add rays to show the shadows the Sun makes when:

a) it is high in the sky

b) it is low down in the sky.

3 Why do we sometimes see a Full Moon and sometimes see a New Moon?

4 Explain what makes a solar eclipse happen.

Remember

Match the words to the spaces.

**source   eclipse   Full Moon   New Moon
rays   straight   shaded   shadows   sunny**

Light spreads out from a light _____1_____. Some objects block the light and make _____2_____. Light travels from the source and past the object in _____3_____ lines. We can trace the pathways of the light with lines called _____4_____. When the shadow of the Moon falls onto the Earth we experience a solar _____5_____. When we look at the Moon and see a bright ball we are looking at a _____6_____. We are looking at the _____7_____ side of the Moon. When we look mostly at the _____8_____ side of the Moon we see a _____9_____.

143

Escape from the Earth

The force of gravity is a force that can act at a distance. Large objects like the Earth and the Sun exert large forces of gravity.

Stars and planets pull strongly on all other objects that are near to them. The force acts on objects that are not touching. We call it the force of **gravity**.

Gravity is a strong part of our everyday lives. It's strange to think that our lives would be very different if the force of gravity were like electric and magnetic forces. Those forces can attract or repel. Gravity is only ever attractive. Try to imagine what life would be like if the Earth attracted some objects and repelled some objects.

Figure 1 Life would be different if gravity could repel.

The Earth is a huge ball with a surface that's covered in rock and water. We spend all of our lives on it. Only a few animals and a few people have been outside the Earth's **atmosphere** and into space. The atmosphere is a layer of air all around the Earth. The first animal to do this was Laika, a Russian dog. In 1957, she was launched up through the Earth's atmosphere into the empty space above. The Russians wanted to see if an animal could survive the journey. There was no air to breathe outside her spacecraft, so the spacecraft had to carry air to keep her alive.

Figure 2 Laika, the first dog in space

Astronauts escape from the Earth's atmosphere into space. But they *don't* escape from the Earth's gravity. Gravity holds them in **orbit** around the Earth.

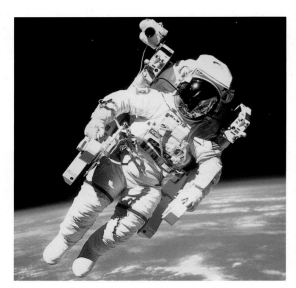

Figure 3 Above the atmosphere, in empty space. But gravity still pulls on these astronauts, keeping them going round and round the Earth.

Only a very few people have ever set foot anywhere except on Earth. Neil Armstrong was the first, in 1969, when he stepped on to the Moon. The Moon has its own gravity. But since the Moon is smaller than the Earth, its gravity is weaker. The Earth and the Moon pull on each other, so that they orbit around each other and travel together through space.

Figure 4 The astronaut Buzz Aldrin sets foot on the Moon. The Moon's own gravity holds him to the surface.

Figure 5 As the Moon is smaller than the Earth, its gravity is not as strong.

Only in stories have people travelled so far that they escaped from the pull of the Earth's gravity.

Figure 6 Adventure in space – away from the force of gravity of any star or planet.

Questions

1 **a)** What is the Earth's atmosphere?

   b) Why did Laika's space capsule need to carry an air supply?

2 **a)** Have you ever escaped from the surface of the Earth?

   b) Do you think that you will ever escape from the Earth's atmosphere?

3 **a)** Why is the gravity of the Moon weaker than the gravity of the Earth?

   b) Describe what you think it would feel like to walk on the Moon, like Neil Armstrong.

4 Draw a picture of the launch of the Space Shuttle or a satellite. Show the rocket motors working.

5 Write about what it would be like to be on a Space Shuttle being launched.

Remember

Unscramble the anagram words to complete the spaces in the passage.

All large objects like stars and planets exert a force of <u>GRAVY IT</u> . The force is always <u>TIE RAT V CAT</u> . The bigger the object, the <u>BRIG EG</u> the force.

We are held on the <u>HES ART</u> surface by its strong force of gravity. Nobody has ever escaped completely from the influence of the Earth's gravity. Some people have been above the <u>AT HER POEMS</u> of the Earth, where there is no air.

Planet hopping

The Sun is a huge star at the centre of a system of planets called the Solar System. The Earth is one of these planets. The Sun's strong force of gravity keeps the planets in orbit around the Sun.

A long time ago, in 1977, a new spacecraft was launched into space. It was called Voyager 2 and it's still travelling today. On its journey it has been past many planets and their moons. Now it's so far away from the Earth and the Sun that there are no more planets for it to visit. It has become the first human-made object to escape from the **Solar System**.

The Sun is by far the largest object in the Solar System. The Sun is at the centre – it is the gravity of the Sun that holds the planets in their orbits. Without this force of gravity, the Earth and the other planets would escape from the Sun. If the Earth escaped then we would lose the warmth of the Sun. We would not receive the energy that plants need to grow, and we would starve and freeze in darkness.

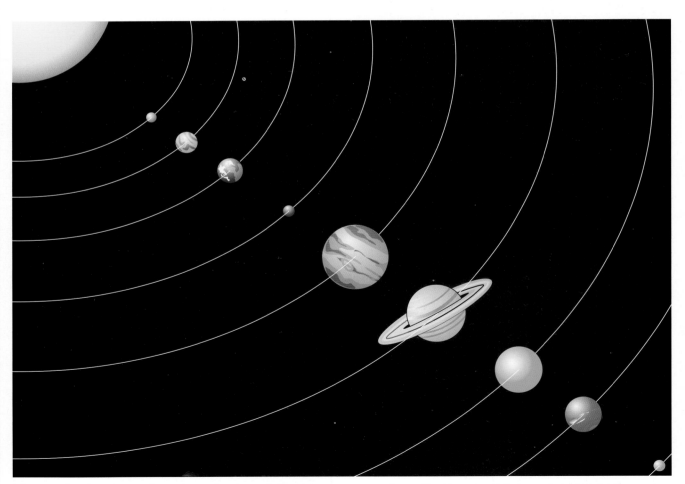

Figure 1 The picture shows how the sizes of the planets compare. In reality, they don't lie in such a straight line and the distances between them are HUGE.

Martian sunset – Mars is further from the Sun than the Earth so the Sun looks smaller from Mars. The picture was taken by the Viking space mission.

The Sun's force of gravity on an object gets weaker as it gets further from the Sun. Voyager 2 has now gone so far away that the Sun exerts hardly any pull at all. There are no stars other than the Sun anywhere near the Solar System. Some distant stars like this may have their own system of planets in orbit around them.

moons of Jupiter

Jupiter is the biggest planet. It is a very different world from our own planet Earth. It is a ball of gas, and because it is so big, its gravity is very strong.

Io is a rocky moon in orbit around Jupiter. It has active volcanoes, just like the Earth.

Pluto is a small planet a long way from the Sun. The Sun's light is weak on Pluto, so it is a very cold planet. This picture was taken by the Hubble Telescope.

Questions

1 If the Sun is just a star, why does it look much bigger than other stars?

2 During its long journey, what has happened to the strength of the Sun's gravity pulling on Voyager 2?

3 a) Why are there no people travelling on board Voyager 2?

b) Do you think that people will go that far one day?

Remember

Complete the sentences below using the following words.

**Sun   orbit   stars   distances
planet   gravity**

The force of gravity acts over very large

_____**1**_____ . It is strongest close to a star or

_____**2**_____ , and gets gradually weaker as you

move away.

The _____**3**_____ is a star. The Earth and the

other planets are in _____**4**_____ around the

Sun. All of the planets are trapped by the

_____**5**_____ of the Sun.

The Solar System is big. But all of the

_____**6**_____ we can see are far outside the

Solar System.

Planet data 1 – other worlds

The Solar System is made up of planets and their moons in orbit around the Sun. We'd find that the planets would all be very different places if we could visit them.

The sky at night, full of stars, is very, very beautiful. People have looked at it and wondered about it for thousands of years. They spotted that some of the small points of light in the sky do not seem to move in a simple way. There were only a few of these and they were given their own name – the **planets**.

In the past, most people guessed that the Earth was the centre of everything. They guessed that the Sun and the planets and the stars all went around the Earth. But that couldn't explain the way that the planets seemed to move in more complicated ways across the sky. Then a Polish monk called Copernicus explained that there was another, simpler way of understanding the planets, the Earth and the Sun. He said that the Earth could actually *be* a planet itself, and that the Earth and the *other* planets were all going around the Sun. Copernicus wrote about the revolutions of the Earth and planets.

This meant that the Earth was not the centre of everything. To the people of Copernicus' day this was an amazingly new idea. Most people didn't like such a new idea. So, even now when someone suggests something so incredibly new, we say that their idea is *revolutionary*.

Nobody has ever seen the sight shown on this page. It is an 'artist's impression' of the whole Solar System, made up of the Sun and the planets with their moons. The Earth and our Moon are just two of the objects in the Solar System, you can see them here near the centre of the picture. The Moon is the furthest that anyone has ever been from the Earth. But by using Copernicus' ideas, humans have sent space missions, with no people on board, to visit planets like Venus and Mars. And we have been able to imagine what the Solar System would be like if we could go outside it and look back. It wouldn't look quite like the picture here because we have exaggerated the sizes of the planets. From outside the Solar System, beyond the orbit of Pluto, the Earth would be too small to see at all.

Earth

Figure 1 Revolutions of the planets around the Sun. This picture also shows a comet. A comet is much smaller than a planet. It moves around the Sun like the planets, but sometimes it is very near to the Sun and sometimes it is very far away. The Sun and the planets are not drawn to scale here.

Planet data

Average distances from the Sun, in millions of kilometres.

Mercury	58
Venus	108
Earth	150
Mars	228
Jupiter	778
Saturn	1430
Uranus	2870
Neptune	4500
Pluto	5900

Number of moons

Mercury	0
Venus	0
Earth	1
Mars	2
Jupiter	16
Saturn	18
Uranus	15
Neptune	8
Pluto	1

Force of gravity on a bag of sugar on the planet's surface, in newtons

Mercury	4
Venus	9
Earth	10
Mars	4
Jupiter	26
Saturn	10
Uranus	8
Neptune	12
Pluto	1

Surface temperature in °C

Mercury	−170 to 400
Venus	350 to 475
Earth	−80 to 50
Mars	−125 to 20
Jupiter	−150
Saturn	−200 to −150
Uranus	−220
Neptune	−220
Pluto	−250

Questions

1 Which of the planets is most like Earth in

a) its distance from the Sun

b) the number of moons it has

c) how heavy a bag of sugar (or anything else) is on its surface?

2 a) Make charts and graphs of the information in the tables on this page.

b) Draw labelled pictures of the planets. Think about the sizes of the planets in relation to each other.

c) Combine all of these together into a poster to go on the wall.

If you have access to a computer, use it to help you with this work.

3 Choose the planet you would most like to visit. Write a paragraph about what you might see if you were on the surface of that planet.

Remember

Match the words to the spaces.

> **Pluto** **Pluto** **smaller** **Moon** **moons**
> **Venus** **planets** **Sun** **forces** **Mercury**

The Solar System is made up of ____1____ travelling around the Sun. Most of the planets have ____2____ . Moons are ____3____ objects that travel close to their planets. The Earth has only one moon, called the ____4____ .

The planets are at different distances from the ____5____ . ____6____ is the closest and ____7____ is the furthest away. ____8____ is the hottest and ____9____ is the coldest. The planets have different sizes. There are different ____10____ of gravity on their surfaces.

Planet data II – seasons on the planets

Different planets have different patterns of days, years and seasons.

The planets are all at different distances from the Sun. So they must make different journeys around the Sun. Mercury is the closest to the Sun. The time it takes to go around once is the shortest. Pluto is the furthest from the Sun and it takes the longest.

As the planets speed through space they also spin, like crazy fairground rides. We spend our whole lives on one of these crazy fairground rides. We speed round the Sun, once in every Earth year. At the same time we spin. It takes just one Earth day to make a complete spin. As we spin, we sometimes face towards the Sun. We have a name for times like that – it's called day-time. It is the spin of the Earth that carries us into light and darkness every day.

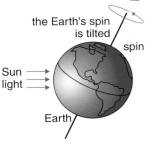

Figure 2 The Sun shines on every planet, but the spin of every planet has a tilt.

Figure 3 The spin of Venus only tilts a little bit. But you could say that Uranus almost 'spins on its side'. The tilt in the spin of the Earth is 23.5°.

Length of the planet's year – the time it takes to travel once around the Sun

		once around the Sun
Mercury	88 Earth days	= 1 Mercury year
Venus	225 Earth days	= 1 Venus year
Earth	365.25 Earth days	= 1 Earth year
Mars	687 Earth days	= 1 Mars year
Jupiter	12 Earth years	= 1 Jupiter year
Saturn	30 Earth years	= 1 Saturn year
Uranus	84 Earth years	= 1 Uranus year
Neptune	165 Earth years	= 1 Neptune year
Pluto	248 Earth years	= 1 Pluto year

Time to spin once, in hours

		one spin
Mercury	1416	= 1 Mercury day
Venus	5832	= 1 Venus day
Earth	24	= 1 Earth day
Mars	25	= 1 Mars day
Jupiter	10	= 1 Jupiter day
Saturn	10	= 1 Saturn day
Uranus	11	= 1 Uranus day
Neptune	16	= 1 Neptune day
Pluto	6	= 1 Pluto day

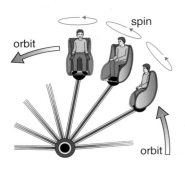

fairground ride – orbits and spins at the same time

Figure 1

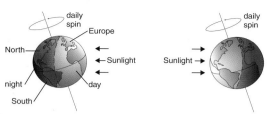

The tilt in the Earth's spin means that for part of each year, the northern half is tilted towards the Sun. The northern half is called the northern **hemisphere**. At this time the Sun shines more from overhead and the weather is warmer. It's called summer. At the same time the southern half is tilted away from the Sun. There the sunshine is not so strong and it is winter. When the Earth then moves half way around the Sun, it's the southern hemisphere that gets the Sun more overhead, and it's the turn of the northern half to have winter.

In the winter the Sun does not rise so high in the sky, because we are tilted away from the Sun. Also we do not spend so much of each day in the light of the Sun. It goes dark in the afternoon, and gets light again quite late in the morning.

At some times of the year the Southern half of the Earth is tilted towards the Sun. In the north we have winter and we spend more of each day in darkness.

When it's Summer in the north we are tilted towards the Sun. We don't spend so long in darkness.

Figure 4 It is the tilt of the Earth that gives us the seasons.

Tilt of spin

Mercury	7°
Venus	3°
Earth	24°
Mars	26°
Jupiter	3°
Saturn	27°
Uranus	88°
Neptune	29°
Pluto	50°

Questions

1 Which planet is most like the Earth in

  a) the time taken to go around the Sun

  b) the time taken to spin once

  c) tilt of its spin?

2 **a)** How many times have you been around the Sun?

  b) If you'd lived all your life on Jupiter, how many times would you have gone around the Sun? What is your age in Jupiter years?

3 On Venus there isn't much difference between summer and winter. Can you explain why?

4 How long is a Neptune year? How long is a Neptune day? On Neptune how could you tell the difference between the summer and the winter?

Remember

Match the words to the spaces.

winter   spin   Earth   year   northern
away   tilted   seasons   hemisphere

The time that the Earth takes to go around the Sun is called one _____**1**_____ .

The length of time that the Earth takes to make one ____**2**____ is called one Earth day.

The spin of the Earth is ____**3**____ . The tilt stays the same all year. Sometimes the ____**4**____ half of the Earth is tilted towards the Sun, and sometimes the southern half is tilted towards the Sun. That is why we have ____**5**____ .

In ____**6**____ we spend longer in darkness, because then it is our ____**7**____ of the planet that is tilted ____**8**____ from the Sun.

Finishing off!

★ The Sun is our natural source of light. Light travels to us in straight lines at high speed.

★ A force of **gravity** holds us to the Earth. Force of gravity also keeps the Moon in orbit around the Earth.

★ The Earth and the Moon are in **orbit** together around the Sun. The Sun's strong force of gravity holds all of the planets in orbit.

★ Force of gravity *always* attracts and *never* repels.

★ The Earth is one of the planets that are in orbit around the Sun.

★ The spin of the Earth carries us in and out of the light of the Sun, once every day.

★ The tilt of the Earth's spin means that sometimes sunshine is stronger in the northern hemisphere and sometimes it is stronger in the southern hemisphere.

Questions

Write a story about an imaginary journey through the Solar System, visiting some of the planets. You could choose just one planet if you prefer. These are some of the things that you could include in your story:

How far will you have to travel? How will the Sun appear from the different planets? Will you have to go to sleep during daylight? How long might you have to wait for it to get light? How heavy will objects be to carry around? How heavy will your body feel? What protection will your body need from the conditions on the different planets? What moons will you see in the 'sky' of each planet? Do you think that any of the planets might have living things on them?

Web sites to visit:

NASA Homepage
   http://www.nasa.gov/

Near Earth Asteroid Rendezvous Mission
   http://near.jhuapl.edu/

Amazing Space Web-Based Activities
   http://amazing-space.stsci.edu/

NASA Space Science Homepage
   http://spacescience.nasa.gov/

Voyager Project Home Page
   http://vraptor.jpl.nasa.gov/

Nine Planets – a guide to the Solar System
   http://www.nineplanets.co.uk/

Glossary

Glossary

Glossary